THE FAITH OF A SCIENTIST

Henry Eyring, 1963.

THE FAITH

OF A

SCIENTIST

HENRY EYRING

BOOKCRAFT
Salt Lake City, Utah

LIBRARY OF CONGRESS CATALOG CARD NUMBER 67-25432

2nd Printing, 1973

LITHOGRAPHED BY
PUBLISHERS PRESS

SALT LAKE CITY, UTAH
UNITED STATES OF AMERICA

Preface

BELIEVERS AND ATHEISTS ALIKE ARE PRONE TO MUDDY the waters of truth in ill-informed discussions on the subject of science and religion. It is refreshing therefore when a scientist of Dr. Henry Eyring's eminence undertakes from the vantage point of his training and observation to outline his views—in this case his deep-seated convictions—on the matter.

The theme of this collection of Dr. Eyring's writings may be simply and briefly expressed. It is that, disregarding the theories and conjectures of the advocates on either side, true science and true religion are and must always be in complete harmony; that this must be so because truth is consistent—no one truth can conflict with another truth; and that the existence of a loving, personal God who offers a beneficent plan for man's eternal progression is not only consistent with scientific truth but is for him as much a reality as any of the findings of science.

Dr. Eyring not only uses his training and talents to contribute to the advance of science but, as a man of deep faith in God, he also gives wholehearted allegiance to the principles of revealed religion. This combination, together with his cogency of thought and facility of expression, has produced in *The Faith of a Scientist* a book which will strengthen the faith of all lovers of truth.

The Publishers

Contents

Foreword

D R. HENRY EYRING, WHO IS AN ACTIVE MEMBER OF The Church of Jesus Christ of Latter-day Saints, declares throughout this book that his research has confirmed his faith in God. He also declares that he has no difficulty in reconciling the principles of true science with the principles of true religion, since both are concerned with the eternal verities of the universe.

Over many years I have indicated to Dr. Eyring that this conclusion confers upon him at once an opportunity and a responsibility—to write the results of his study and conviction for the benefit of others. This he has done in articles printed in *The Instructor*, the official magazine of the Deseret Sunday School Union of whose general board he is a member, and in *The Improvement Era.*

President Johnson's 1967 presentation to Dr. Eyring, together with ten other scientists, of the United States' highest award for scientific research and achievement stimulated other friends and myself to obtain copies of articles he had had printed in these two journals and to invite him to add to this collection other of his writings which confirm the great declaration that there is no conflict between true science and true religion. When we approached him on this he expressed his willingness to have these articles published in book form in the hope that they might help others to reach the conclusions that have brought him peace and happiness.

I take great satisfaction, as I hope the reader will, in knowing that a scientist of such stature as to receive the National Medal of Science is also a devout and active Christian church member. From my personal experience I know that Dr. Eyring not only believes, but tries to live the way of life advocated and exemplified by the Master, Jesus Christ.

The accounts in the first part of this book outline the attainments and honors which had come to Dr. Eyring by the time the accounts were written. Since that time he has raised the number of his published scientific papers to four hundred and the number of his honorary doctor's degrees to eight. Dr. Eyring's writings comprise all but the first part of this book.

At this critical time in history I believe this book will help to stimulate an increased faith in God, which is a vital need for the peace, happiness and progress of the world.

Dr. Francis W. Kirkham

Salt Lake City, Utah
April 1967

PART I

Henry Eyring
The Man and the Scientist

Henry Eyring—Distinguished Scientist and Churchman

by
Marba C. Josephson[1]

To KEEP THE FAITH AND YET MOVE FORWARD IN THE field of science is not irreconcilable, but it has proved difficult for some people. In Dr. Henry Eyring we find the desirable combination of a great scientist, for he was selected by readers of *Chemical Bulletin*, a professional publication of the American Chemical Society, as one of the ten leading authorities in the field of physical chemistry—and a stalwart believer in The Church of Jesus Christ of Latter-day Saints. As he states:

> For me there has been no serious difficulty in reconciling the principles of true science with the principles of true religion, for both are concerned with the eternal verities of the universe.

Probably it would be well to delve into the background of the man whose brilliance has placed him and, through his loyalty to it, the Church of which he is an active member, in such high esteem that one of his colleagues at Princeton University said on the occasion of

---

[1]This article was published in February 1948 by *The Improvement Era*, of which the author was associate editor.

Dr. Eyring's farewell dinner (in an oblique reference to Gospel discussion between the two):

> I have defended Mormonism among a community of Jesuits and pride myself on the issue, though, of course, I had the great advantage that came from earlier argument "about it and about."

Born in Colonia Juarez, Chihuahua, Mexico, on February 20, 1901, Dr. Eyring went through the difficulties of the exodus when he was eleven years of age, at the time when so many of the Saints were driven from their homes. With his parents, Edward Christian and Caroline Romney Eyring, and their family, which includes Camilla Eyring, wife of Spencer W. Kimball of the Council of the Twelve, he settled in Pima, Arizona. The Eyring family has always been unusually active in the educational field, and Henry was no exception. He obtained a B.S. degree in Mining Engineering in 1923, and an M.S. in Metallurgical Engineering in 1924, both from the University of Arizona. The following year he was instructor in chemistry at the same university. In 1925 he enrolled in the University of California at Berkeley, from which institution he received his PhD in chemistry in 1927.

From here he went directly to the University of Wisconsin, where he was instructor of chemistry the first year and a research associate from 1928-29. Here, interestingly enough, the current of his life was enriched through his meeting of Mildred Bennion of Granger, Utah, who had obtained a year's leave of absence from the University of Utah—where she was assistant professor in health and physical education—in order to do further study in her chosen field. She, too, knew the value of education, for she had lost her father when she was seventeen and had diligently worked to equip herself as a teacher. Her year's leave of absence from the University of Utah was extended permanently when she met Henry Eyring, for they were married in Chicago, August 25,

1928, going through the Salt Lake Temple, December 21, 1928. The following year they went to Europe on their belated working honeymoon, while Dr. Eyring attended the Kaiser Wilhelm Institute in Berlin as a National Research Fellow (1929-30).

This marriage has resulted in great teamwork, understanding and happiness, and from the marriage have come three upstanding boys: Edward Marcus, 17 at the present time (1948), a high school student and a priest in his priesthood quorum; Henry Bennion, $14\frac{1}{2}$, a teacher in his priesthood quorum; and Harden Romney, $8\frac{1}{2}$.

Following the year spent in Germany, Dr. Eyring became a lecturer in chemistry at the University of California for the school year of 1930-31. In 1931 he joined the staff of the department of chemistry at Princeton University where he remained until August of 1946, when he accepted the position of Dean of the Graduate School at the University of Utah.

In addition to his work as professor of chemistry at Princeton University, Dr. Eyring served as research director of the Textile Research Institute for the years 1944-46, at which time two main projects were under investigation: a study of the chemical properties of textile fibers, and a study of the bleaching and general molecular deterioration of textiles because of chemical reaction. During World War II he also did research work for the Army, Navy, and O.S.R.D., on the theory of smokes and on the theory of high explosives.

Dr. Eyring's major fields of specialization include radioactivity, the application of quantum mechanics to chemistry, the theory of reaction rates and the theory of liquids. In these various fields he has published in the neighborhood of 150 papers together with special chapters in various chemistry books. He is co-author with Samuel Glasstone and Keith J. Laidler of the book, *The Theory of Rate Processes* (1941), and, with John Walter and George Kimball, of *Quantum Chemistry* (1944).

Dr. Eyring's accomplishments have won him great honors. He has been vice president of the American Association for the Advancement of Science, chairman of its chemical section, and recipient of the ninth award of the same association in 1932. He has also held offices as secretary and chairman of the Division of Physical and Inorganic Chemistry of the American Chemical Society and as vice president of the Society of Rheology, and is associate editor of the *Textile Research Journal.* He holds membership in the National Academy of Sciences, the American Philosophical Society, the Textile Research Institute, Sigma Xi (college honorary society for scientific students), and the Utah Academy of Sciences, Arts and Letters. In May 1947, he became the fifth person to receive the University of Arizona Alumni Achievement Award.

And what of Dr. Eyring's Church activities during this full life of academic achievements? He has never allowed his Church affiliations to suffer, no matter how strenuous his collegiate endeavors may have been. He has always been not only an active member wherever he has gone, he has also taken an active part in the functioning and direction of the Church. While in Berkeley, he was called into the presidency of the high priests' quorum during 1930-1931; he served as president of the New Brunswick Branch from 1932 to 1944; and as district president of the New Jersey District from 1944 to 1946, when he moved to Utah. Since that time, Dr. Eyring has been an outstanding addition to the general board of the Deseret Sunday School Union.

Dr. Eyring has evidenced by his life and his works both in Church and in his chosen profession—the sincerity of his belief in the restored gospel. He has expressed the conviction that there should and must be spiritual development along with intellectual achievement. His own life, which typifies this conviction, is a monument to faith in The Church of Jesus Christ of Latter-day Saints.

Henry, Edward Marcus (standing), Harden Romney, Henry Bennion and Mildred Bennion Eyring.

Henry Eyring, President-Elect

by

Carl J. Christensen[1]

"**P**HYSICAL CHEMISTRY IS EVERYTHING THAT IS INTER-esting." So replied G. N. Lewis, the distinguished mentor of Henry Eyring at Berkeley, California, when queried about the content of this scientific discipline. If this definition be correct, then one who follows the profession of physical chemistry must be sort of a "pan-scientist," and for this title Henry Eyring is well qualified.

It is entirely appropriate that a scientist of this description should lead the American Association for the Advancement of Science, for this organization, by its very title, must be presumed to be engaged in that broad front of truth-seeking and truth-dissemination which applies no limiting adjectives to describe the word science.

Henry Eyring, the man, is as interesting as Henry Eyring, the scientist. He is a product of the 20th century, having been born in February 1901 in the little pioneering community of Colonia Juarez, Chihuahua, Mexico, some hundred miles south of the United States-Mexican border and near the Mexican town of Casas Grandes. Colonia Juarez had been founded by a colony of U.S.

---

[1]This article was written in 1964, when Dr. Eyring was named president-elect of the American Association for the Advancement of Science, and published in *Science*, February 21, 1964. The author was then professor of chemistry and ceramic engineering and coordinator of cooperative research at the University of Utah.

citizens, including all the grandparents of Henry Eyring, who left southern Utah in search of more land which could be used for ranching. Growing up in such a community, young Henry became a youthful "cowpoke." I have seen the broad range on which Henry, as a lad, "rode herd" on unwilling range cattle, and have listened to stories of frustrating, and therefore memorable, occurrences on this range.

But this cattle range was not to be involved in Henry's future. In the words of Robert Burns, "The best laid schemes o' mice and men gang aft agley," and in Henry's case a turning point in his life came when the Mexican rebel, Salazar, threatened the little "Yankee" colony with extermination, causing the inhabitants to flee north to El Paso and safety. Henry was 11 years old at the time and he has never forgiven his elders for not permitting him to ride out on horseback with the hastily formed militia, rather than be sent out on a train with the women and children.

The experience left the family impoverished, since they left behind them all their possessions. Under the circumstances, Henry took his first job for hire and became a cash boy at Calisher's Department Store in El Paso. Henry reports that his beginning wage in this store was $2 per week and that this was soon raised to $3.50. His work week was 63 hours. Even this small wage helped support the family in this time of difficulty. The original idea of the family was to go back to their Mexican holdings as soon as the trouble subsided, but, instead of the expected improvement the conditions there became worse and the family decided to make a new home in Pima, Arizona, a town of a few hundred people a short distance from Thatcher, in which a good high school existed.

Henry excelled as a high school student and won the $500 scholarship from Graham County to study at the University of Arizona. With this scholarship and extra money made by "waiting table" at the University, he was able to obtain his bachelor of science degree in mining engineering. It must be remembered that in those days mining in the west was a glamour activity and held the promise of romance for a young mining engineer. During the summer months Henry worked as a timberman in one of Arizona's copper mines, but the experience was not to his liking and caused him to reorient his objectives. After graduation he obtained a graduate fellowship at his Alma Mater and went for a master's degree in extractive metallurgy; his thesis dealt with the rapidly developing subject of flotation. After receiving his master's degree he took an engineering job in a smelter, but this also failed to satisfy him, and even though he was given an alluring promise of rapid promotion by the smelter superintendent, he went back to the University of Arizona where he joined the department of chemistry for a year and did a research problem in quantitative analysis. The following year found him at the University of California (Berkeley) as a teaching assistant in chemistry. He received his doctoral degree in 1927; his thesis was concerned with a problem in radiochemistry. G.E. Gibson was his major professor.

After graduation, Eyring went to Wisconsin as an instructor in chemistry. Here he came under the influence of Farrington Daniels, and was oriented toward reaction rate theory, to which area he has contributed as much as, and possibly more than, any other scientist. While at Wisconsin, Henry met and married Mildred Bennion, so that his two years at Wisconsin were important ones in shaping his adult life.

The 1929-30 academic year was spent as a National Research Fellow in Haber's laboratory in Germany where Eyring worked with Polanyi in pioneering the calculation of activation energies and in developing the first potential surface on which a quantitative theory of reaction rates was later built. The year 1930-31 found Eyring again at

Berkeley as a lecturer where he did the work on hydrogen-halogen reaction rates which showed for the first time that reaction rates could be predicted from theoretical considerations. This work brought him such favorable attention that H.S. Taylor offered him a staff position at Princeton University where he remained until 1946, when his interest in the needs of the West caused him to go to the University of Utah as dean of the newly organized graduate school. There he helped to build an important graduate program in Mormon country, the land to which his "converted grandparents" had emigrated from Germany and England.

Henry Eyring is a genealogist by instinct and is proud of his ancestry. Besides the Eyring family from Coburg, Germany, his ancestry includes the von Blomberg family from Prussia and the Bomeli family from Switzerland—each a family of substantial and intelligent people. From them comes Henry's bias toward science. His mother comes from the Cottam and Romney families of England. Many of these individuals show great talent for business, for political leadership and for athletics, as currently illustrated by his cousin George Romney, governor of Michigan. Henry has the athletic abilities of the Romney family though he has never "gone out" for athletics, as many of his cousins have done. His athletic interests are now satisfied by frequently walking the two miles from his home to the university, by an occasional mountain climb, and by a yearly foot race with the graduate students. He treats them to a banquet after the race, regardless of their success in the race.

The Eyrings have three sons, each of whom is an excellent and serious-minded student. The eldest boy, Edward M., is following his father as a physical chemist and is also at the University of Utah. His special interest at present is that of very fast reaction rates. The second boy, Henry B., is at Stanford University as an assistant professor of business administration, and Harden, the youngest, is a graduate student in physics.

During his years as university lecturer and professor, Henry Eyring has directed the doctoral thesis work of no fewer than 64 graduate students, many of whom now are numbered among the world's highly productive scientists. These students have sought out Eyring with whom to study because he is always stimulating, comes easily by novel and productive ideas, is solicitous of the progress of his students, rewards them liberally with commendation for their earnest efforts to solve difficult scientific problems, and is generous in giving the student status by making him the senior author on joint publications.

Eyring's training was that of an experimentalist, but his contributions while at Princeton were almost exclusively in the realm of theoretical chemistry, wherein the published experimental results of others became the bases of illuminating analyses which led to new concepts and increased understandings of wide-ranging scientific phenomena. Hideki Yukawa, Nobel prize winning physicist from Japan, in his memoir of a trip around the world, entitled "Micro-World," has this to say of his visit to Eyring's laboratory at Princeton:

> I visited Professor Eyring at Princeton, N.J., in May, 1940. . . . It was the first time to meet Dr. Eyring, although I had known him for a long time through his interesting papers in quantum theory. He was younger than I expected. After talking about his current researches, he showed me around his laboratory and introduced his students to me. I saw only slide rules and several calculators on tables, but could not find even a simple piece of experimental apparatus in his laboratory. It was my first experience to observe such a chemical laboratory.

Regardless of the observations of Yukawa, Eyring's theorizing usually has as its incentive and purpose the explanation and understanding of observed and measured phenomena. At the University of Utah, he is building a laboratory of his own which now has in it several expensive and exotic pieces of equipment to study optical rotatory phenomena and the reactions of materials in high pressure environments.

The facile way Eyring's mind works in arriving at the solution of a scientific problem is a dynamic and stimulating experience for one who watches him think through a problem with chalk in hand before a group of students.

The services of Eyring are widely sought as a speaker in several areas: as an expositor of recent scientific developments to groups of professional scientists, as a discussant of science and religion to church groups and to college students during the "religious emphasis weeks" of their various institutions, and as an interpreter of science to lay groups, including high school students. During Christmas week (1963) he gave the first series of five popular lectures on science at the Franklin Institute in Philadelphia; these lectures have been described as a revival of the famous Faraday Christmas lectures given at the Royal Society of London over a century ago. Eyring's style and manner of speaking must be characterized as unorthodox, but his discussions are always lively, informative, stimulating and enjoyable. His unique sense of humor—which is always at the expense of himself—is extensively used in his lectures to lay groups and makes attendance at the lectures a delightful experience.

Eyring always has on his agenda a work load which would frustrate most individuals. To meet his many appointments, he travels much and in this seems indefatigable. He relaxes easily so that he can rest well on a plane, on a train, in an airport—in fact, almost anywhere night finds him, so long as it is warm. He says he is a Mexican and needs only warmth to be able to rest.

Henry Eyring came to the University of Utah in 1946 as the first dean of the graduate school of that institution. In the intervening 17 years the graduate school registration has grown to about 2,000 students a year. A recent survey by the U.S. Office of Education places Utah as number 40 among the graduate schools of the country in the matter of doctor of philosophy degrees bestowed in the 10-year period from 1949 through 1959. Because this statistic includes the very lean years when this program was just beginning at the University of Utah, the present standing of the University must be higher than this. As graduate dean, Eyring is sensitive to the needs and problems of the graduate student and is much more considerate of those in difficulty than are many of the younger heads of departments who think an excellent graduate school can only develop if the faculty is "tough" on students. Students who draw a reprimand from Eyring usually do so because of an infraction of the usual code of honesty and integrity, or the evidence of laziness.

The scientific publications of Eyring are extensively read and frequently referenced by other scientists. This is so probably because these publications are readily understood and the results are applicable to a wide variety of scientific phenomena. Eyring's solution to a problem usually begins with an easily understood physical model to which he applies the necessary mathematics in order to arrive at a quantitative and usable answer. Neither the method nor the answer is involved with mathematical minutia and uninterpretable symbolism; where mathematical approximations ease the way, these are used. With Eyring, mathematics is a tool and not an end. The physical and chemical nature of the problem, or the answer, is never submerged in mathematical obscurity. To develop a suitable model, Eyring frequently asks: "Now how would I act if I were an atom and found myself in this environment?" Such a question usually brings forth an interesting model on which to work for a quantitative result. If agreement is not attained, a new model is postulated.

The breadth of Eyring's scientific contributions is

partly indicated by the many scientific disciplines to which he has been a direct contributor. These include: mining engineering, metallurgy, ceramics, fuels, explosives, geology, plastics, fibers, lubricants, organic chemistry, molecular biology, analytical chemistry, radiation chemistry, electrolytic chemistry, quantum chemistry, and statistical mechanics. Most of Eyring's papers use the physical-chemical approach to the problem involved, and most have to do with the energy and time description of the making and breaking of chemical bonds, which is the most universal phenomena in the mundane world. The work of Henry Eyring gives confirmation to the comment of G.N. Lewis at the beginning of this biographical sketch.

The number of publications carrying Eyring's name an an author or co-author now number about 350. These have appeared in many journals from several countries. Among these publications are four books, three of which are classics in their field. A new book entitled *Statistical Mechanics and Dynamics* is now in press and several more are in course of being written, including one to be entitled *The Dynamics of Life*. In addition, Eyring is a director of "Annual Reviews, Inc.," and the editor of the series, "Annual Reviews of Physical Chemistry."

Many scientific societies include Eyring in their membership rosters; these include the National Academy of Sciences, the American Association for the Advancement of Science, the American Chemical Society, the American Philosophical Society, the American Academy of Arts and Sciences, and the Society of Rheology.

He has been an officer in several of these, including: president, American Chemical Society (1963); and vice president of the Society of Rheology (1946). Presently he is head of Section 15 (physical chemistry) of the National Academy of Sciences Committee for the National Bureau of Standards. He was appointed by the National Academy of Sciences to prepare the molecule demonstration for the U.S. exhibit at the Brussels World's Fair in 1958. In 1962, President Kennedy appointed him to the National Science Board, and he is a member of the Scientific Advisory Committee of the Welch Foundation of Houston, Texas. It seems appropriate to mention here also that he serves his church as a member of the General Board of the Sunday Schools of that organization. He takes considerable pride and delight in this activity, and the assignment has taken him on Sunday School matters throughout the United States, England, Mexico, and Canada. This church assignment is his only deviation from complete dedication and service to science.

For his distinguished contributions to science, Eyring has been given honorary doctoral degrees by five universities. The American Chemical Society has honored him with the Debye award in physical chemistry (1964); the California Section, the G.N. Lewis award (1963); the New York Section, the William H. Nichols medal (1951); and the Utah Section their Annual Award (1959). The University of Arizona bestowed upon him their Alumni Achievement award (1947) and their Award of merit (1960). The Society of Rheology bestowed upon him their Bingham Medal (1949). The initial recognition of Eyring's merit, however, was by the American Association for the Advancement of Science which bestowed on him the 9th Annual prize (1932), and now they honor him with the highest recognition to be bestowed by them, the president-elect of the Society, which leads to the offices of president and retiring president and chairman of the board of directors.

Peter Debye once said of Eyring, in effect: "His contributions to science are like the paintings of Frans Hals; he paints with a bold, broad brush." In presenting Eyring with the Research Corporation award, Joseph W. Barker said: "He has pushed hard and successfully into the previously unknown and, like Jason, has brought home the Golden Fleece. He is a true catalyst of men's minds. In his presence, ideas just naturally flow and methods of disproving them are originated." Hugh S. Taylor once commented: ". . . he possesses the Midas touch. Everything in scientific research turns to gold when brought to the attention of his fertile brain. But there are none of the evils that beset the original Midas."

The scientific contributions of Eyring are well known to his peers and recognized by them as important contributions to the onrush of scientific knowledge. Men everywhere, who enjoy the bounties of science, are blessed with these bounties partly because of the contributions of Henry Eyring which have had and will have a part in making scientific and technological progress possible.

PART II

Religion ,Science and Truth

Science and Faith

I HAVE BEEN ANNOUNCED AS A STUDENT OF SCIENCE. BUT I also like to think of myself as one who loves the Gospel of Jesus Christ. For me there has been no serious difficulty in reconciling the principles of true science with the principles of true religion, for both are concerned with the eternal verities of the Universe.

And yet there are many people, and particularly among our youth, who regard the field of science and the field of religion as two wholly different spheres, the one entirely separated from and unrelated to the other. In fact, there are those in both fields who have done themselves and the causes to which they give their interests a distinct disservice in teaching that the two are opposed and that they cannot be harmonized one with the other.

So I would like to address my remarks to those who find themselves troubled by an inner conflict between the traditional teachings of Christian faith on the one hand, and on the other the challenge of modern education to explore, to dissect and to test in the cold light of fact and demonstrated proof. I believe that many of our young people have impoverished their lives by a thoughtless denial of all aspects of the faith of their fathers in their desire to be what they call scientific and objective.

Now I am also of the opinion that some theologians have unwittingly assisted in this rebellion by taking positions so dogmatic as to stifle the honest and thoughtful inquiries of youth when they needed help and sought it.

I should like to say that true religion was never a narrow thing. True religion concerns man and the entire universe in which he lives. It concerns his relationships with himself and his fellow men, with his environment, and with God his Creator. It is therefore limitless, and as boundless as that eternity which it teaches lies ahead of every son of God. "Be ye therefore perfect, even as your Father which is in heaven is perfect." What a challenge to every man lies in these words from the Master— to develop himself, to strive, to learn, to seek, to go forward that he might become as God.

Man in his ceaseless search after truth has discovered and partially explored five worlds. These worlds differ from each other in the size of the units of space and time we need to describe them. In our everyday practical world, we get along nicely with such units as feet and seconds. In the chemical world of molecules and atoms, the electrons complete their revolutions in a hundred million millionths of a second, while a hundred million atoms side by side extend only a distance of one inch. Inside the nucleus of the atom, we enter a third world, where events happen a million times faster still, and distances are a thousand times smaller than in the atom. In the fourth world, the astronomers measure revolutions of the planets in years, and the unit of distance, the light year, is about ten thousand million miles. Finally, we come to the spiritual world where time is measured in eternities and space is limitless. Thus, in thought we can travel from the almost infinitesimally small to the infinitely large.

Now, curiously enough, there are good people who would have you believe that man, who conceives all these wonderful things, and masters them in part, is no more than the dust of the earth to which his body returns. To me, this is unbelievable.

I am happy to represent a people who throughout their history have encouraged learning and scholarship in

all fields of honorable endeavor, a people who have
among their scriptural teachings such lofty concepts as
these: "The glory of God is intelligence, or in other
words light and truth." "It is impossible for a man to
be saved in ignorance." "Whatever principle of intelligence we attain unto in this life, it will rise with us in
the resurrection."

To us has come the following which we regard as a
divine injunction:

> Teach ye diligently and my grace shall attend you,
> that you may be instructed more perfectly in theory, in
> principle, in doctrine, in the law of the gospel, in all
> things that pertain unto the kingdom of God, that are
> expedient for you to understand; of things both in heaven
> and in the earth and under the earth; things which have
> been, things which are, things which must shortly come to
> pass; things which are at home, things which are abroad;
> the wars and the perplexities of the nations, and the
> judgments which are upon the land; and a knowledge also
> of countries and of kingdoms. (Doctrine and Covenants
> 88:78-79.)

Here is the spirit of true religion, an honest seeking
after knowledge of all things of heaven and earth.

In times of uncertainty, such as the present, the
increasing effort to understand man's place in the grand
scheme of things proceeds at an accelerated pace. That
understanding is a problem not alone for the laboratory;
many of its answers will be found in the realm of the
spiritual. It is important that all men of good will use
their energies, their talents and their learning in their
chosen fields, mutually assisting one another toward the
building of a better world—that world which men of
faith in all ages have envisioned and toward which they
have labored.

Now, of course, the scientist is not in general a
specialist in questions of religion. But that need not mean
that he is not a believer in the great principles of Christi-

anity. Many of the noted pioneers in the scientific world were men of faith whose learning in their chosen fields seemed only to strengthen their sense of a great spiritual realm beyond their ken.

To attempt to choose the greatest among scientists is always a rather ambiguous and questionable procedure, but among mathematicians, Archimedes, Newton, and Gauss are usually ranked first.

About Archimedes' religious ideas very little is known, but the other two have revealed their attitude. Touching on Newton's position, the mathematician E.T. Bell, in his book *Men of Mathematics,* says: ". . . Newton was an unquestioning believer in an all-wise Creator of the universe."

The great mathematician Gauss indicated his view when he said:

> There are problems to whose solution I would attach infinitely greater importance than to those of mathematics; for example, touching ethics, or our relation to God, or concerning our destiny and our future.

Others might also be cited to illustrate that there is no inconsistency in being both scientist and believer. It would be folly, of course, to maintain that all men who have achieved eminence in the scientific world have been religious men. But I think that most of them have had the humility and the frankness to acknowledge that there are forces in the lives of men, and influences which may be brought into their lives, which are both real and potent, although they, the scientists, may have had no personal acquaintance with those forces within their own experiences.

Most of them, I believe, would not presume to say that a thing may not be because they do not understand it, nor would they deny the validity of spiritual experiences of others because they have been without such experiences themselves.

It is interesting to inquire what methods are open to him who seeks religious truth. The four gospels tell the story of the Son of God who came into the world, lived an exemplary life, died, and was resurrected. If accepted as accurate, this record puts the necessity of being religious beyond question. History, unlike laboratory experiments, cannot be tried over again, just because we are not quite sure what the happenings meant. In this sense, religion differs from such laboratory sciences as chemistry and physics, and is more iike astronomy or historical geology, where we must depend in part on inference. In the end, however, if the inquiry is broad enough and careful enough, we need be no less sure of our final conclusions.

The Lord himself outlined the procedure when he said: "If any man will do his will, he shall know of the doctrine, whether it be of God, or whether I speak of myself." (John 7:17.)

I would like to suggest to the youth who may feel inclined to disparage religion as he pursues other studies, that he might bring enrichment to his life by cultivating faith and an interest in things of the spirit as he follows his other pursuits. Such faith will never detract from his abilities in other fields, but it will broaden his thinking and give added depth to his character.

I am now going to venture to say that science has rendered a service to religion. The scientific spirit is a spirit of inquiry, a spirit of reaching out for truth. In the final analysis, this spirit is likewise of the essence of religion. The Savior said: "Ask, and it shall be given you; seek, and ye shall find; knock, and it shall be opened unto you." (Matthew 7:7.) The scientist has in effect reaffirmed this great fundamental laid down by the Master, and in doing so has given a new impetus to religion.

Science has also in effect strengthened religion by assisting in sifting the grain of truth from the chaff of imagined fable. It is interesting to recall that in ages past, religious men felt that their faith hinged on the notion that the earth was flat. However, when it was found to be round, they discovered that their basic religious ideas had survived without perceptible damage. In fact, the great underlying principles of faith were brought into bolder relief when the clutter of false notions was removed from about them.

More recently, we have been obliged to give up the old determinism of classical mechanics as well as the idea of indestructibility of matter. Mechanical determinism meant that if one were given the state of the universe at any instant of time, a sufficiently expert mathematician could calculate the state of things at all times to come. This left no place for the great religious principle of free will. Then quantum mechanics brought with it the uncertainty principle. This principle eliminates the possibility of predicting the future exactly, and tends to confirm that fundamental Christian tenet that man enjoys free agency as a divine gift.

The atomic bomb dramatically emphasized a fact discovered earlier in relativity theory and in laboratory experiments. This fact is that matter can disappear only to reappear again as energy. This liberalization in our conceptions regarding matter gives added significance to the doctrine that the spirit is composed of a refined kind of matter.

Just as science has proved a help to religion, so religion in its finest expression has given impetus to science. I should like to quote again from what we accept as modern scripture:

> That which is of God is light; and he that receiveth light, and continueth in God, receiveth more light; and that light groweth brighter and brighter until the perfect day. (Doctrine and Covenants 50:24.)

If I detect any great fundamental principle in the Christian religion, it is the principle of eternal progression—that there is no end to the progress of a man who seeks truth. Death is not the end; it is but one more step in a great forward march made possible by the redemption wrought by the Savior. This is the spirit of true science—constant and eternal seeking.

Nor is that all. The Christian doctrine of the worth of the individual has largely made possible the freedom under which science has flourished. It is a matter of great concern to men of science that liberty over the earth is being restricted, and as liberty becomes restricted, untrammeled research will narrow. I am grateful that I have lived in a time when a man could do largely as he chose to do and in a land where he could map out his way and follow it. I consider it one of the greatest blessings that has come from our Christian civilization, and I believe that it has made us great as a people.

In conclusion, I should like to make one other point. The scientific method which has served so brilliantly in unraveling the mysteries of this world must be supplemented by something else if we are to enjoy to the fullest the blessings that have come of the knowledge gained. It is the great mission and opportunity of religion to teach men "the way, the truth, the life," that they might utilize the discoveries of the laboratory to their blessing and not to their destruction. There is need for added spirituality of the kind that leads to brotherhood, to go hand in hand with the scientific progress of our time.

God grant that in seeking the mysteries of His handiwork, we may also learn His great religious truths, which we have been prone to disregard, that our efforts might become a blessing unto us.

The Gospel
and Modern Science

THE WORK OF RENE DESCARTES AND SIR ISAAC NEWTON typifies two methods of attack on the problems of science.

Descartes attempted to build up a universal system which would explain all the problems of nature from a unified philosophical point of view. He was quite willing to go far beyond what he could demonstrate experimentally, provided the point of view seemed rational to him. He thought everything, even problems of physiology, should be explained in terms of mechanisms. Most of his ideas on physics have been superseded by the painstaking method of careful observation. He fared better in the field of mathematics where he verified his results as he proceeded.

Newton, on the other hand, was careful in his law of gravitation, in his mechanics and in his theories of optics to proceed slowly and to avoid going beyond what he could prove. Thus, imperfect measurements of others led to estimates of the moon's force of attractions to the earth one-sixth greater than was correctly predicted by Newton's theory. As a result, he waited years to resolve this difficulty before publishing his theory. The result is that most of what Newton published still stands. Relativity and quantum mechanics simply extend Newtonian mechanics without superseding it in the realm for which it was developed.

In religion, too, there are two ways of proceeding. There are those truths we know by revelation and by long experience. Then there are the myriads of problems which are interesting but go far beyond the things we know. One type of mind goes plunging into the mysteries and explains them all to his own satisfaction. This probably does little harm, if one doesn't end up believing one's own daydreams. It is just as important to keep fact and fancy separated in religion as in science.

Perhaps in no way is the apostasy clearer than in the wedding between what was left of early Christianity with Greek philosophy as it developed in the Middle Ages. Thomas Aquinas, for example, undertook to weave all knowledge into a single consistent scheme to support his religious convictions. He leaned heavily on Aristotle and wove what is now very bad mechanics into some of his proofs of the existence of a Creator. The result is a philosophy shot through with palpable error. Perhaps the believer never does more disservice to religion than to support the truth with bad arguments. The impatient listener, perceiving the obvious errors, often "throws out the baby with the bath" and turns away, even from true religion.

The erroneous conception that revelation ended with the apostles promotes the misconception among sectarian religions that the Gospel is complete and that with a liberal admixture of human wisdom, all will be crystal clear.

The Restored Gospel teaches, rather, that certain things are known by revelation and by study, but much more remains to be learned. God in His wisdom will reveal more as the need arises. We are engaged in a never-ending program of eternal progression. Don't judge us in terms of what we now know. We'll be much wiser after some expert teaching in the hereafter.

In spirit, the wise Latter-day Saint is much nearer to Newton than to Descartes. Like Newton, he sees far because he stands on the shoulders of giants. The endless road to perfection is marked out by the prophets, but he doesn't yet know all the answers by any means.

The measurement of time is an interesting field in which there has been enormous progress. We have come a long way since the time when the sundial and the hourglass were useful means of telling time. For example, the ammonia molecule is made of a nitrogen atom with three hydrogen atoms sticking out from it like the three legs of a stool. This molecule automatically turns wrong side out like an umbrella in a windstorm some ten thousand million times per second. By accurately tuning radar equipment to ammonia molecules, we get an instrument which measures small fractions of a second more accurately than this was ever done before.

If we wish to measure time in hudreds of years, we have, besides tree rings and the annual deposits of sediment in lakes, the new radioactive clock, carbon 14. Recently much work has been done on radioactive carbon 14 which is continually being formed in the atmosphere by cosmic rays and is likewise decomposing at a steady rate. The result is that it forms a constant very small proportion of the carbon in the atmosphere which is present as carbon dioxide. This carbon dioxide is absorbed by the plants and built into the cellulose which forms their woody parts. In the atmosphere, the decaying carbon 14 is being continually replenished by formation of new atoms from cosmic rays. This replenishment ceases in the non-growing wood.

The result is that in the first 5,500 years, half the radioactive carbon from wood or cotton disappears and in another 5,500 years half of what remains disappears and so on. The amount present at any time thus indicates the antiquity of the object. The result is that the time when any tree or piece of cotton grew can be established within two hundred years. This method can be cross-checked on dates known by other means.

In analogous fashion, uranium and radium in the rocks change into lead at a known rate so that if we want clocks that tick off million-year intervals, we simply determine how far this change has gone in a particular rock formation and can thereby tell when the rocks containing the particular clock were laid down.

All these wonderful findings in nature should increase our reverence for the omniscient wisdom of the Creator in fashioning this exquisitely complex universe as a school for His children. Since the Gospel embraces all truth, there can never be any genuine contradictions between true science and true religion.

This doesn't preclude the need, however, of thinking through the inter-relationships between religion and science as new interesting discoveries are made. When properly done, the result is necessarily a deeper appreciation of divine goodness and of all the truths of the Gospel.

Our Six Worlds

A LITTLE OVER A HUNDRED YEARS AGO PETROLEUM WAS discovered, and since that time the use of power has increased about 1500 per cent. America's national income has increased in almost exactly the same proportion. Our gross national product in 1967 will be about 700 billion.

This is no accident. The five-and-one-half horsepower working in the United States for each individual is equivalent to forty slaves per person. No wonder we live better than the richest Greek or Roman with all his slaves. This has all been made possible by science and invention. We shall continue to develop and grow along these lines just so long as we continue to support our educational and research institutions. Whether these material blessings are used for good or ill, however, depends upon our character and upon our understanding of the physical and spiritual forces operating in the world around us.

We, in this age, live in six worlds. They can be represented by a point surrounded by five circles.

The first, or central, world is the world of the *atomic nucleus* and of the atomic bomb. The nucleus where most of the weight of an atom is situated has a diameter less than one ten-thousandth that of the atom. Vibrations inside the nuclei of atoms are about a million times more frequent than the vibrations between atoms.

The second world is the world of *chemistry*, made up of atoms and molecules. This is still a tiny world. It would take just 100 million atoms placed side by side to reach an inch. A molecule finishes one of its vibrations in about a ten million millionth of a second. We call this length of time a "jiffy" for lack of a better name.

Our third world is the world of the living cell, the world of biology. Cells vary in size but typically they are about a micron across, that is about one ten-thousandth of a centimeter. An active cell divides into two cells about every twenty minutes. The human cell has near its center a cell nucleus containing forty-six chromosomes. Twenty-three of these come from the father and twenty-three from the mother. The chromosomes are made up of about a million genes which constitute our inheritance. A gene controls the synthesis of essential molecules such as enzymes which build and regulate our unbelievably complicated bodies.

The fourth world is the world of *everyday*. Here, we measure time in seconds or minutes and distances in feet or miles. This is the rorld we know most about.

If we next look at the *stars*, we see the fifth world. By using the largest telescope, we can see out so far that the light reaching our eyes started on its journey toward us almost two-and-one-half billion years ago. Scientists estimate that this is back toward the beginning of our present universe.

The sixth, or the *eternal* world, includes and surrounds all the others. In it we know neither beginning nor end of space nor of time. Presiding over all is the Creator whom we worship. Holding everything together are the eternal laws which will require an eternity for us to master. Such is man's prospect; such is his destiny.

Contemplating this awe-inspiring order extending from the almost infinitely small to the infinitely large, one is overwhelmed with its grandeur and with the limitless wisdom which conceived, created and governs it all. Our understanding, great as it sometimes seems, can be nothing but the wide-eyed wonder of the child when measured against Omniscience.

These observations about the universe can be sum-
marized under five headings:
1. Grandeur
2. Orderliness
3. Running Down
4. Purposefulness
5. Immanence of the Creator

Thus, we are part of a grand scheme embracing all
of creation, complicated and orderly beyond our most
extravagant dreams. In it, there is the order of immutable law. Eclipses and certain atomic interactions can be
calculated with any desired degree of accuracy. The
universe has been likened to a fine watch, unexpectedly
picked up in a desert. One might assume the watch was
assembled by accident, but the only reasonable assumption is that it had a creator who left it there. So it is
with this magnificent universe. It is obviously more
complicated than a watch since it contains watches.

Another startling fact about the universe is that it is
running down. Our sun is about half hydrogen. This
hydrogen is the fuel which burns in the solar furnace to
helium, which is the ash left by the conflagration. This
burning which is happening all the time on the sun
happens if hydrogen is placed properly in an atomic
bomb—provided, of course, that the bomb reaches sufficiently high temperatures and pressures.

As with any woodpile, if you keep burning up the
hydrogen on the sun, it must ultimately be used up
unless it is replenished. There is evidence that in the
last billion years the sun's temperature has not varied by
the small amount which would make the earth unfit for
habitation. Scientists believe that in the normal course
of events, it will be longer than billions of years before
the sun scorches or freezes all living things.

If one picked up a watch far from human habitation
and found it running, one would ask not only who made
it, but also who wound it up. So it is with this universe.

It was not wound up by chance, but by some as yet unfathomed operation of eternal law.

We come now to our fourth point. In this universe governed and created according to eternal laws, is it likely that the most intelligent creatures in it are here by chance? The great measure of the Restored Gospel is that the Creator not only made the world but that He made it for His children and that He is still actively interested in a program which was not completed two thousand years ago, as is sometimes supposed.

The revelations to the prophets, both ancient and modern, testify to the immanence, or closeness, of God to His children. His guiding hand is to be seen in all creation by those who are sensitive to the influence of His Spirit. In fact, there are two ways of drawing nearer to Him: first, through the intellectual contemplation of God's handiwork; second, through spiritual communion with the Creator in which we gain direct experience of His presence. The Latter-day Saint who lives up to his opportunities will do both.

Communication

WHEN A PERSON RECEIVES INTELLIGENCE FROM THE Lord and is willing to communicate that for the benefit of the people, he will receive addition to that intelligence." (Lorenzo Snow, *Journal of Discourses* 5:64.)

Human beings are born into the world with great potentialities but no learning. The knowledge which makes the difference between civilized man and the untutored savage flows to us from others in an unending stream from birth until death. All of us are involved in this process of communication, and the well-being of society measures directly how well the job is being done.

The industrial world we live in would fall apart without the intense intercommunication of information through advertising. The American standard of living exceeds the most extravagant dreams of our pioneer forefathers. Power machinery provides each of us with the work of forty slaves. Mass production, made possible by the advertising which promotes mass consumption, has created this magic world where the American laborer lives better than did ancient kings.

The Gospel, in all its beauty and perfection, is effective also only as it is communicated. In each generation, the Gospel needs people like the Apostle Paul to proclaim it for all to read and to hear. His epistles have brought faith and hope to millions. They fairly vibrate with the faith and ardor of this great apostle. Not all of our great religious leaders, however, have been blessed with this gift of communication. How many of us, like Moses, when commissioned to lead Israel from bondage, say, "It

*Henry Eyring addresses American Institute of Metallur-
gical Engineers on Steelmaking in Pittsburgh, August 27,
1959.*

is too difficult—for I am slow of speech"? (See Exodus
4:10.) Exemplifying in a superlative degree the over-
coming of this barrier to communication is Miss Helen
Keller. *Life* magazine carried a picture of the seventy-
three-year-old, smiling Miss Keller with her hand pressed
against President Eisenhower's face, following his reactions by touch. She has been without sight and hearing
for seventy years. One can scarcely imagine more complete isolation. Yet, with the help of her teacher, Ann
Sullivan, and others like her, Miss Keller did the impossible and learned to communicate her thoughts better
than many who have no special handicap.

Communication of information involves both a sender
and a receiver. The Gospel flows out from the Creator of
the world who sees the end from the beginning. It flows
out to all who are able to receive it. Too many of those
who are blind and deaf to this flow of information fool-
ishly deny the existence of the Creator. How much
wiser they would be if like Helen Keller, they could
overcome blindness and deafness and reach out and touch
Him.

Written in the many languages of the world are all
sorts of messages which escape us completely because
we don't speak that particular language. We have not
found the appropriate Rosetta Stone. The Creator of the
universe has implanted a message in every created thing.

Geologists search for the meaning to be read into the
piled-up strata of the earth much as an historian might
turn the pages of an ancient, damaged manuscript. The
astronomer seeks the answer to his questions in the depths
of space. Still other men concentrate on the scriptures
alone. The wise man searches all these and other sources,
knowing that all are communications from the same
divine source and certain that, if followed far enough, all
will guide him back to the divine Presence.

The scriptures give us a clear understanding of the
concern of the Eternal Father for His Children. In both

ancient and modern scriptures man has received divine communications which establish the religious pattern for those who heed it. When one contemplates the immensity of space, one cannot help marveling at the wonderful methods of communication still remaining to be discovered. The wisest physicists know no method of transferring messages faster than the speed of light. In fact, built into the theory of relativity is the idea that matter and energy, as we know them, never travel faster than light.

The universe is so large that the best reflecting telescopes enable us to see stars by light which started journeying toward us two-and-one-half billion years ago. The subsequent history of these stars is completely unknown. They may long since have ceased to exist. There seems no reasonable alternative to the conclusion that the Creator has methods of communication which travel by other means and at speeds unknown and perhaps unknowable to mortal man. Somehow, the universe is coordinated and regulated by influences which transcend the laws of physics now known to man. Nor should this seem strange if one remembers that such marvels as radar, radio and the telegraph were unimaginable a century and a half ago. What wonders can we not hope to unravel in the endless eternity ahead? It is interesting to note that Orson Pratt raised this same question regarding divine communication and answered it in much the same way about a century ago. Though our knowledge of the universe is always expanding, the fundamentals of the Gospel endure unchanged.

Religion in
a Changing World

L ET US CONSIDER A LITTLE THE NATURE OF TRUE GREAT-
ness in men. The people who catch hold of men's
minds and feelings and inspire them to do things bigger
than themselves are the people who are remembered in
history. The cold person who simply propounds some
logical position, however important and interesting it
may be, cannot do for the Lord's children what is done
by those who stir feelings and imagination and make
men struggle toward perfection. On this basis, Joseph
Smith stands very far up on the scale on which the
Savior is paramount.

Let us next consider a few of the things that are
striking in the teachings and life of Joseph Smith. Joseph
grew up in a world that was narrowly sectarian. In this
cramped world, he taught that man had lived eternally
and would always live. This idea of a pre-existence was
startling in that day, as it is in this.

Plato spoke of a pre-existence, but we learn from the
Prophet Joseph that man lived before he was born; that
life is a school where man is sent to learn the things the
Lord intends; and that he continues on into life after
death. Immortality is in the very nature of things. As
intelligences, we always existed. What a tremendous
influence these ideas have had! No wonder people build
towns and chapels all over the world in honor of this
great latter-day teacher. There will be many more wards
and stakes as monuments to this great man.

Another idea that the Prophet taught was revolutionary. In place of the idea of placid membership in a heavenly choir, we have the concept of eternal progression. There is no limit to how high man, the spirit child of God, may climb. By hard work, by study, by constantly increasing in humility and in wisdom through the eternities, we will approach perfection. This great idea can't help firing our imaginations.

In still another way he loosened the shackles that bind men's minds. The School of the Prophets was formed. He obtained the best teachers available and studied and learned all he could and promulgated the idea that the Gospel embraces all truth—that truth is to be accepted whatever its source. It is difficult to see how anyone could hear such teachings without being deeply affected.

One of the problems of the Church is the unsound arguments sometimes used in its defense. People examine such arguments, find they won't hold water, and say, "My, the Gospel must be unsound." The conception that the Gospel should only be defended on the right ground is of utmost importance, since otherwise one may choose a position to defend which is indefensible; and in defeat it may be mistakenly supposed that the Gospel is at fault.

Once when I was speaking at the University of Utah as part of a panel on "Man in the Cosmos," I built my talk about the famous question of Pontius Pilate, "What is truth?" After the talk, which covered various aspects of man in the cosmos, a young man in the audience stood up and said, "Well, Dr. Eyring, they tell me that what you do is put your religion in one compartment and your science in another. Isn't that inconvenient? For instance, I want to propound a question to you. In the Young Women's Journal, Joseph Smith is reported to have said that there are people living on the moon." He continued, "Now, Dr. Eyring, we know there is no oxygen on the moon, so that couldn't possibly be true. What do you say to this question?"

I answered about as follows: "I especially appreciate being asked that question, because it is easy to answer, and I like easy questions better than hard ones. As a Latter-day Saint, like any other honest man I am obliged to accept only the truth. I simply have to investigate whether men live on the moon. I am reasonably certain they don't, but anyway, we'll soon know by direct exploration. If we don't find them there, they don't live there. As a Latter-day Saint my problem is as simple as that.

"I want to add a few more thoughts. Many times men of importance have statements attributed to them they never made. I think that if J. Golden Kimball said all of the things he is credited with saying, he would have had to talk even more than he did, and he did very well.

"Now what about the Prophet Joseph Smith? I don't know whether he said men live on the moon or not. But whether he did or not troubles me not in the least. A prophet is wonderful because he sometimes speaks for the Lord. This occurs on certain occasions when the Lord wills it. On other occasions, he speaks for himself, and one of the wonderful doctrines of this Church is that we don't believe in the infallibility of any mortal. If in his speculations the Prophet thought there were people on the moon, this has no effect on my belief that on other occasions, when the Lord willed it, he spoke the ideas that the Lord inspired him to say. It is for these moments of penetrating insight that I honor and follow him."

There is a further point that needs emphasis. The Gospel is not the people in the Church. The Gospel is not even the people who direct it. *The Gospel is the truth.* One will have difficulty finding better men than we have presiding over the Church at present and than we have had in times past. Still, they are human beings as we are.

In this connection, I should like to say another thing. Some people have pointed to some member of the Church and said, "Now, Dr. Eyring, that's one of your brethren, and he's not what he ought to be." My answer is this,

"Well, you ought to see what he'd be like if it weren't for the Church." We have to keep firmly in mind at all times the two aspects of the Church: its divinely inspired perfect side, and its human side.

Perhaps I can say it another way. This Church would have been perfect if the Lord had not let people into it. That is where the mistake seems to have been made, but we understand this too. The Church is part of His wonderful plan to work with you and with me. Mankind is thus singled out because of man's divine origin and transcendent destiny.

Let us next develop some of the points where the Gospel provides a uniquely beautiful and satisfying explanation. The arguments are old, but they are still interesting. As one looks out at the universe, the first impression is one of stupendous size. It takes light two billion years to reach us from the farthest stars that can be seen in the best telescope. This telescope happens to be on Mount Palomar in southern California. You remember how fast light travels: 186,000 miles a second; it goes around the earth, a distance of 24,000 miles, seven and one-half times in a second. If you multiply 186,000 by the number of seconds in two billion years, you get 135 followed by seventeen zeros for the number of miles you can see in any direction you care to look. Presumably, the only reason you do not see farther is the fault of the telescope, not that there are not more distant stars to see. The known radius of the universe in miles is even bigger than the national debt. It is a very long distance indeed.

God, whom we worship, understands all of the things that go on in a universe which extends more than two billion light years in each direction. I like to compare the universe with my holdings. The comparison is instructive. My wife and I have a lot which is sixty feet across the front, one hundred feet deep, and extends straight up to the limits of space, so far as I know.

Clearly, this qualifies me to speak on the broader aspects of the universe. Actually, man rooted to his little plot of earth can only stand in utmost awe of the all-powerful Arbiter of the universe.

The vastness of the universe and the majesty of its Creator are arresting points. Also, we live in a universe governed by exact natural laws—a world of order. There are many ways of discussing this point. One of them is to recall the great triumphs of Sir Isaac Newton, who discovered the universal law of gravitation and developed the laws of mechanics so that his successors have been able to calculate the motion of the planets in their orbits to any desired degree of accuracy. Astronomers predict exactly when an eclipse will occur. Using this knowledge, men make great preparations, assemble expensive scientific equipment and move to the ends of the earth when told that an eclipse is imminent. They get their cameras ready to take the pictures, open the shutter at the right moment and the eclipse begins at the predicted instant. If the eclipse were ever so little off schedule, this would make headline news around the world. Here we are treated to two miracles: first, fabulously exact laws exist; and second, man has the genius to unravel these mysteries and reduce the existing order to codified laws which he then manipulates in the service of mankind.

A Latter-day Saint needs to understand that the Creator of the universe is great beyond anything imaginable, but it always adds to this deeper understanding of the Gospel to see that we are able to partake at least in some degree of His greatness and shape an orderly world to our needs.

These same laws that enable astronomers to compute eclipses tell precisely, of course, how a satellite goes around in its orbit. A man who makes a good running broad jump only misses becoming an earth satellite by not running fast enough. Thus, if instead of running twenty miles an hour he ran 20,000 miles an hour he would find that as he jumped, the earth would curve away beneath him faster than he could fall toward it. Our jumper would settle into an elliptical orbit extending around the earth, except for one thing—the air resistance would slow his speed down and set him on fire. To avoid air resistance, the satellite is shot above the atmosphere. This is the only reason for sending it up 600 miles. Satellites like Sputnik and the moon have a terrifically frustrating job. The moon has been falling toward the earth and overshooting the mark for billions of years and still has no prospect for a successful hit. Man has not succeeded in sending satellites up to such complete frustration yet. The reason is simple. They get up there 560 miles, even a thousand miles, sometimes, but there is still a trace of hydrogen left. As the satellite circles the earth, it bumps into gas. When it has bumped into a weight of gas equal to its mass, its momentum is cut in half, except that by falling closer to the earth it picks up additional speed.

Using the known laws of science, one can calculate exactly how much hydrogen there is at any altitude, providing the temperature is known or assumed. Knowing the amount of hydrogen, one can establish the correct temperature. Thus a falling satellite is in this sense just a very fancy thermometer. Still, it is a remarkable human achievement to launch a satellite in the sky and in a small degree to become a partner in creation. This fits into our idea of eternal progression. We believe that eventually the children of God will increase in wisdom beyond any assigned limit.

Consider one further example of the exactness with which this universe works. Ammonia consists of a nitrogen atom sitting on three hydrogen atoms. The startling fact is that this umbrella-like molecule turns wrong-side out almost twenty-four thousand million times a second. If you beam radar through a tube containing ammonia, the signal fades just when the radar frequency equals the inversion frequency of the molecules. In this way, the ammonia molecules can be used as a clock to break time up into twenty-four thousand millionths of a second with unprecedented accuracy. Now it is interesting that this ammonia molecule turns wrong-side out just as often whether you are at room temperature or at the lowest temperatures you can get in the laboratory; whether you are in Soviet Russia or the United States; and whether this country is Democratic or Republican.

I want to digress a moment to recall a remark which the Prophet Joseph Smith made and which people sometimes forget: every blessing you get in this life is predicated on obedience to some law. If you want some particular blessing, the Lord has arranged this very exact world so that you get the blessing only if you work for it. The communist with his ghastly doctrine that the end justifies the means can work with ammonia just as we can. Further, there is no reason to suppose the molecule will ever wear out. In fact, if we could prove that it does wear out, it would be a major contribution to contemporary physics.

Here again we see the exactness with which this universe operates and the magnificent laws which govern it.

In mentioning something of the effect of this exactness on the minds of people, what it does to them, I will recall an incident that happened to me. A Mr. Robert A. Welch died, leaving ninety million dollars to develop chemistry in Texas. Each year the Welch Foundation invites a group of the world's top scientists to a symposium in their specialty. In 1957, the symposium dealt with the physics and chemistry of the nucleus. Twelve of these top scientists were dining at a table when the question "Do you believe in a Supreme Being?" was broached. By common consent, the group was polled. Twelve out of twelve said, "I believe."

The result was interesting to me. To explain this

unanimity, the following seems important. Exact scientists are deeply impressed by the precision with which natural laws apply. Any explanation which ignores a Planner leaves this fact unexplained and is therefore unacceptable. I think scientists from some other discipline farther removed from the exact sciences might not have voted with such unanimity.

I wouldn't want it supposed that there aren't very able scientists who are atheistic, but they are certainly much in the minority. La Place, one of the very great physicists, when asked by Napoleon why his great book on the origin of the universe failed to mention Deity, said, "Sire, I have no need for that hypothesis." This is another point of view.

I have talked about the magnitude and about the exactness of the universe. There is a third point that should be developed. This is a universe of change. People are born and pass from the earth, and stars also come into existence and pass away. The sun is about half hydrogen; the rest of it is composed of other materials, and the hydrogen bomb shows us what happens to hydrogen down in the center of the sun where the pressures and temperatures are enormous. We know what has to happen. Four hydrogen atoms come together to make helium, and in the process, a little of the weight is changed into energy. This is the energy which falls on the earth as sunlight and makes the green plants grow. Thus the sun is a giant furnace with a supply of hydrogen for fuel—quite a good supply. But if the sun ever burns out it is going to be very difficult in Logan. We need an estimate of the supply on hand. I would say the supply should last at least five billion years, so we don't need to worry about it right away. If the sun is needed beyond that time, the Power that created it in the first place can undoubtedly renew it.

This picture of the sun as a furnace with a limited amount of fuel poses interesting problems. The second law of thermodynamics is a formal statement of the familiar fact that if energy, such as sunlight, is being produced continuously from some source, such as the sun, then the supply of energy must run out sometime unless it is replenished from an outside source. In a very real sense, then, the universe is like a clock which has been wound up. If it is self-winding, it is unique in scientific experience. In a talk before the National Academy of Sciences, I raised the obvious question, "How did the universe get wound up?" No one chose to answer. After the talk, I repeated my question privately to three scientists. President Millikan of California Institute of Technology said, "I, like you, am a religious man." Professor Van Vleck of the Harvard physics department said, "Of course, one doesn't know." The third man said, "Don't you believe in your religion?" I answered, "Yes, but I wondered about yours."

Again the impression made on me was that scientists generally believe there must be a Supreme Being. In any case, I worship the Being responsible for this magnificent universe, including our solar system with a sun provided with hydrogen which burns with such delicate accuracy that in over a billion years, life, with its tremendous sensitivity to heat and cold, has apparently continued to exist.

Consider next a fourth point. There is apparently purpose in the universe. It is difficult to believe that whoever was wise enough to organize the universe in the first place would not have been wise enough to anticipate the course it would take. Believing this, one comes to questions concerning man. In spite of all man's shortcomings and limitations, consciousness, as exemplified by the depth of man's ability to think and to feel, sets him apart from all other living creatures. Indeed, the scriptures tell us that we are created in the image of God.

It is unthinkable that the Creator should be unaware of man's existence. On the contrary, it must be supposed that we are here as part of an integrated plan designed with regard for our needs and in fulfillment of the divine purpose. God, who notes even the sparrow's fall, must be especially mindful of His children. And so I come as a scientist to this notion of a universe with purpose.

Finally, we come to a fifth point. Accepting as fact the existence, interest and purpose of the Creator, it must follow that whenever it accords with His purpose, we will be made aware of His presence. He is immanent in the world. Although I have never experienced miracles, I have frequently felt keenly aware of an overruling Providence. This feeling of communion with the infinite amounts to certain knowledge on occasion. The first meeting in the newly-built Monument Park Wardhouse was such an occasion for me. On another occasion, it seemed to me that I was directed to our wardhouse in Melbourne, Australia. Another time in Atlantic City, at an American Chemical Society meeting, I seemed directed to meet a fellow church member attending the same meeting. Such feelings of nearness to the unseen Presence are shared by many people and bring abiding faith. This is the great gift for which we should pray.

Faith comes from living the Gospel. Practicing Gospel principles brings an inner peace—the gift of the Holy Ghost—that can be obtained in no other way. The stirring story of Paul on the road to Damascus and the experience which changed him from an implacable foe of the saints to their foremost defender is as compelling now as it was then. No explanation of these events is as satisfying to me as Paul's own interpretation. He gladly dedicated his life to proclaiming the Gospel and at the end went unflinching to a martyr's death. Was he mistaken? I believe not.

Joseph Smith's story is strikingly similar. His experiences in the Sacred Grove and in many places afterward removed all doubt from his mind. For him also, a life of dedication led to a martyr's grave. Was he mistaken?

I believe not. Sometimes people talk about how untrained he was, and that is true. He came from humble beginnings, but he was a tremendous man. The Lord did not choose just anybody to restore the Gospel of Jesus Christ. Joseph was foreordained from the beginning. It was his high destiny and great privilege to restore again to the world the Gospel of the New Testament.

The Lord is not interested in the Latter-day Saints alone. The Gospel is for all of His children. This leads us to a sixth point. Those who understand the Gospel have the special responsibility of sharing this understanding with others. The special message we have comes out of Joseph Smith's mission. Revelation has the same place in the Church now as anciently. When man has used his faculties to do what he can for himself, he can look to a higher source for inspiration and help. As Paul spoke of the law as being a schoolmaster, so we think of the Church as a school to guide us along the road of eternal progression. It is the divinely inspired best way, and as such, is of paramount importance. Joseph Smith restored this best way.

This is a brief outline of some of the points which convince me that there must be a divine church and that I belong to it. There are many reasons for being sure that this is true. And yet there are questions. One that I would raise is the nature of revelation. And what do we mean by saying that the Bible and the Book of Mormon are inspired? The scriptures record God's dealing with His prophets and they are as accurate as He, in His wisdom, requires. They are spiritual guides to religious questions and treat only incidentally scientific and other non-religious questions. In these areas, they should be supplemented by all relevant information. Viewed in this light, most problems disappear. I am obliged, as a Latter-day Saint, to believe whatever is true, regardless of the source. Questions involving pre-Adamic man, organic evolution, or who shall be given the Priesthood at present, are interesting and important questions. They will all receive adequate answers in accord with the truth in due course. Whatever the ultimate answers are, the Gospel will remain and new questions will take the place of those we solve. For me, the truth of the Gospel does not hinge on such questions, interesting as they are.

There are other interesting questions. When you start looking around and deciding whether the Church is true because one of the brethren does not do quite what you think he should, I can tell you a better place to look. See what you yourself are like. Maybe that is why you think the Gospel is not true. If I can keep Henry Eyring doing what he ought to do, I am sure the Gospel will seem wonderful.

This Gospel, the part of it that the Lord is responsible for, is perfect. The rest of it is a lot what you and I make it. If you want to preach, you will do a lot more toward influencing other people by living like the Savior than by developing any kind of fancy arguments.

People ask me, "Well, now, have you converted anybody?" And I say, "Well, I doubt it, but I'm thankful that no more people have apostatized than have on my account. At least I try to live as well as I can, and I try to get the main points first." I try to see what the Gospel really depends on. I try to keep from worrying about the kind of things I am not sure about. If I start arguing about them, I'll get it half wrong and maybe nearly all wrong—because I don't understand them. These matters are unfinished. They will be clarified in due course.

In summary, I am a convinced member of this great Church which the Prophet Joseph Smith had the privilege of restoring in 1830 because of the grand ideas that he brought into the world: (1) that we lived before we came here; (2) that we progress eternally; (3) that if we live as the Savior lived, we preach a greater sermon than anything we can say.

Joseph Smith replaced the narrowness of the sec-

tarian ideas of his day with the idea of a broad education
and set an example of reaching out as far as he could
into all kinds of questions. He gathered around him men
who were outstanding. Prominent among them were the
Smiths, the Pratts, the Youngs, the Richardses. I think of
these great men who were with the Prophet daily, particularly men like Orson Pratt with his acute scientific
mind, and I think that in a certain sense I have walked
down the streets of Nauvoo because people who think as
I do did just that. They were impressed, and they came
away with the feeling that it was really the Lord's work.
There was something to his message; it was really true;
the Lord had spoken to Joseph as He did to Paul long
ago. For these reasons, I feel that the Gospel is more
important than anything else a man can have.

May the Lord bless us to appreciate the life of the
Prophet Joseph Smith and the wonderful message that
he brought to us with the restoration of the Gospel of
Jesus Christ to the earth. May we live and understand it
in a big way and not worry about the small things that
we do not understand very well, because they will become
clearer as we go on. May we have faith, as I have, that
this Gospel has only begun to grow. The things we
believe are only a part of the things that are yet to be
revealed, and if we do our part, our position is sure. We
will indeed be exalted in the celestial kingdom and have
the blessings which the Lord has promised for those that
are faithful.

Wisdom—
Human and Divine

SCIENTIFIC KNOWLEDGE HAS REACHED AN EMINENCE unknown to our forefathers. Unmatched material comforts are combined with a great understanding of the inner working of things. More impressive than what we already know are the systematized methods of scientific investigation. The nation's scientific leaders mapped out a campaign to design and produce atomic and then hydrogen bombs and each project has been carried through with utmost dispatch. With each new discovery, the skeptic finds less need for God, while the devout Latter-day Saint sees in it one more evidence of His overruling hand.

It was ever so. The Bible speaks of the four corners of the earth. In the time of Columbus, there were those who thought a flat earth was a religious necessity. When it turned out to be round, Christ's teachings were found to be just as consistent with the new view as with the old. Later, when Galileo verified the theories of Copernicus and said the earth moved about the sun and so could no longer be considered the center of creation, there were bigots ready to burn him at the stake. When the smoke of battle cleared away and men looked at matters calmly, it became apparent that nothing essential had been lost. A lot of human philosophy disappeared, but it turned out to be unnecessary.

Sir Isaac Newton was deeply religious. The law of gravitation and the system of mechanics which bears his

Henry Eyring addressing University of Utah Alumni of Los Angeles, April 14, 1961.

name were interpreted by him as powerful new manifestations of the divine order of things. To many, Newton's findings have been a continuing source of faith but, again, there were those who were skeptical. La Place, who worked out the first mathematical theory of physical creation, the nebular hypothesis, pointed out, probably correctly, that if the atoms of which a person is made obeyed Newtonian mechanics, then a sufficiently expert mathematician could predict each person's every thought and act. La Place did his work during the time of the French Revolution, around the close of the eighteenth century and the beginning of the nineteenth. All through the nineteenth century, many scholars believed in strict predestination, since a person's acts seemed strictly predictable.

At the beginning of the twentieth century, Max Planck of Germany discovered that Newton's laws just do not apply to atoms. In fact, atomic behavior is uncertain enough that strict predestination of a person's actions, in the mathematical sense of La Place, just isn't so. The probability of various acts of the individual could be calculated by a sufficiently good mathematician, but exact prediction is out of the question. Some learned philosophers have thus felt that this chapter in physics has a bearing on the problem of free will. Whether or not this is so, free will involves additional questions. What is certain, however, is that scholars are continually learning more about the world we live in. In spite of this, when they go beyond what they can strictly prove, they are just like the rest of us. They are guessing. The moral is—believe everything scholars can strictly prove and suit yourself about the rest. Their guesses, like other people's, are often right.

There is another side to this question. As parents and teachers, we pass on to our pupils our world picture. Part of this picture is religious, and part of it deals with the world around us. If we teach our pupils some outmoded scientific notions which fail to hold water when they go on to the university, we run grave risks. When our understudy sheds the bad science, he may also throw out some true religion, i.e., "throw out the baby with the bath." The solution is to avoid telling them the world is flat too long after it has been proved round.

In this connection, I have never ceased to appreciate the fact that my parents, although devout, were never dogmatic. On a September evening in 1919, I was helping my father with the last load of hay before leaving in the morning to study mining engineering at the University of Arizona. He said, "Son, you don't have to accept anything that isn't true to believe the Gospel. Learn all you can. If you live clean and are not profane, you will stay close to the Gospel. If you will do these things, I'll be satisfied with the result." This was just the right thing to say.

At the present time, much is known about the make-up of the human body. It is composed of exactly the same kinds of atoms as make up earth, air and water. It starts as a single cell, too small to see, and by incorporating the molecules in foods, it grows to maturity and after death, returns completely to the elements from which it was made. One can study the chemistry of the living cell just as one studies the chemistry of sugar, flour, or water. The body is a magnificent machine. The skeptic says this is all there is to it. The devout believer says yes, the body is a wonderful machine, but this is only part of the story. Coupled with it is an immortal spirit with a pre-existence. The spirit dwells in the earthly tabernacle as long as it is a fit abode, and at death goes on its way. To resolve this question we must go beyond the methods of science. Science has nothing to say one way or another about whether there is a spirit. This is simply to say that the evidence lies outside of our present scientific knowledge. The scientist, of course, being an ordinary human being, has his own particular estimate of the evidence, like anyone else. But for his opinion to have special weight, he must qualify on other than strictly scientific grounds just as other people must.

If we try to classify that part of religious experience not susceptible to controlled experiment, we can separate it into at least two categories. First, there are the direct experiences of the individual, and second, the evaluations of these experiences by others.

To those who believe in an overruling Providence interested in the individual, it is self-evident that communications will be received whenever it fits into His plans—not necessarily ours. Those with direct experience will find that the painstaking sifting of evidence, which is necessary for their less-favored brethren, is both dull and tedious. This direct awareness of the Creator is promised, in the scriptures, to all those who live for it. Multitudes serenely anchor their future on this certainty of an overruling Providence.

Another avenue to religious faith lies in the examination of evidence. "By their fruits, ye shall know them" is a test to which the Restored Gospel is daily subjected. The perfection of its organization, the prophetic correctness of the Word of Wisdom, the humanity of the welfare plan, the unmatched missionary system, its incomparable youth program, its unpaid officers—all these bespeak the essential soundness of an organization set up during the thirty-nine short years of the life span of its founder.

The interpretation of history is another avenue to faith. Paul, on the road to Damascus, had an experience which changed him abruptly from a bitter opponent of Christianity to perhaps it foremost living exponent. Paul was manifestly intelligent and sincere. Was he mistaken or was his interpretation of the circumstances the correct one? Here one must interpret history. To agree with Paul is to be deeply religious. Joseph Smith's experiences parallel those of Paul in most essential points. The same problem of interpreting history arises. Again, to agree is to find that deepened religious meaning in all human experience.

Pre-existence, immortality, eternal progression, universal brotherhood, continuity of the family, continuing revelation, belief in a personal God, and the necessity of good works, as well as faith—these are a few of the teachings of modern and New Testament times which form the cornerstone on which the good life has been and will be erected by the faithful. To the believers, this kind of evidence, which goes beyond science, is overwhelming in its impact on their lives. To those who cannot see the way, the Gospel still guarantees the right of dissent. This is a wonderful world indeed for those who can see clearly or, lacking this, are able to walk by faith.

Mathematical Concepts and the Gospel

THE GOSPEL EMBRACES ALL TRUTH. OUR PROBLEM IS to weave interesting old and new facts into a scheme to guide us here and hereafter. When we try to think carefully we frequently end up with ideas that are very important and yet are familiar notions in mathematics.

One of the oldest mathematical problems is to find the ratio of the circumference of a circle to its diameter. Stated concretely we may ask, "What is the ratio of the distance around the earth to the distance through it at the equator?" (We of course assume the earth is a perfect sphere for this calculation.) The usual symbol for this ratio is π given to it by the famous mathematician Leonard Euler. One of the oldest answers to this problem is in I Kings 7:13,13: "And King Solomon sent and fetched Hiram out of Tyre. . . . And he made a molten sea, ten cubits from the one brim to the other; it was round all about . . . and a line of thirty cubits did compass it round about." This gives correctly the first term of an endless series namely $\pi = 3$. Actually π is now known to hundreds of places. Some people have devoted much of their lives to determining it more and more accurately. We will give it to 28 places.

$$\pi = 3.1415926535897932384626435883 \ldots \ldots$$

An equation which enables you to calculate π to as many places as you please is found by putting $\theta = \dfrac{\pi}{6}$ and x = ½ in the equation

$$\theta = \sin^{-1} x = x + \frac{x^3}{3!} + 9\frac{x^5}{5!} + \cdots + \left(\frac{d^{n-1}(1-x^2)^{-\frac{1}{2}}}{dx^{n-1}}\right)_{x=0} \frac{x^n}{n!}$$

Any college student who has studied calculus should be able to verify this result in a few minutes using Mac-Lauren's expansion. This expansion is based on the methods of calculation discovered by the deeply religious Sir Isaac Newton.

If you insist on knowing π exactly, you are asking for the impossible, since the series never ends. Thus you can know the answer to as many places as you please and therefore to any desired degree of accuracy, but the question "what is the exact value?" would take an eternity to answer. The statement that we can never know everything about the Gospel is thus a mathematical certainty, since here is one truth which has no answer in finite terms. There is an endless number of such questions without an exact answer. "What is the value of the square root of 3?" is another example. Still another is the question, "How much exactly will you ultimately know?" Some questions take, literally, forever to answer. We recognize an essential truth from these simple examples in mathematics. By diligent study—in the example above by using a computing machine—we can get a better and better idea of the true picture. But to ask for the *whole* picture is meaningless—we can't get it in a finite time. Some people think this last statement means we can't get any of the picture—and so throw up their hands and veil their eyes to understanding anything. We see from our arithmetic examples the contrast of the two ideas.

The following series of operations may seem somewhat abstract but is easily understandable.

$$1/.1 = 10; \quad 1/.01 = 100; \quad 1/.001 = 1000$$

and finally in the limit

$$1/0 = \infty \text{ or } \infty \times 0 = 1.$$

Here 0 is the limiting value which any quantity approaches but never reaches as it gets smaller and smaller. While infinity, ∞, is the limit a quantity approaches but never reaches as it gets larger and larger without limit. In the same way

$$2/.1 = 20; \ 2/.01 = 200; \ 2/.001 = 2000$$

and finally in the limit

$$\frac{2}{0} = \infty \text{ or } \infty \times 0 = 2.$$

Thus we see $0 \times \infty$ can equal 1 or 2 or any other number and therefore the product $0 \times \infty$ is completely undetermined. In passing to the limit we have completely lost the power to give a value to the product of $0 \times \infty$.

Something very like this passing to the limit has happened in certain religions which speak of the Creator as sitting on the top of a topless throne. One religion has this creed. "There is one true and living God, Creator and Lord of Heaven and earth, almighty, eternal, immense, incomprehensible, infinite in intelligence, in will and in all perfection, who as being one, sole, absolutely simple and immutable spiritual substance, is to be declared as really and essentially distinct from the world, of supreme beatitude in and from himself, and ineffably exalted above all things which exist, or are conceivable, except himself." Here we see the example of throwing up hands and saying that we can't understand anything about the problem—that all is veiled from us—because we can't get everything.

President Clark in his book *On the Way to Immortality and Eternal Life,* chapter IV, points out how completely this view departs from that recorded in the New Testament. We will quote only a few passages and refer the reader to President Clark's book for more. The Bible says, "and God, said, Let us make man in our image, after our likeness. . . . So God created man in his own image, in the image of God created he him; male and female created he them." (Genesis 1:26,27.) Further

Jesus said: He that hath seen me hath seen the Father."
(John 14:9.)

Clearly the Bible portrays the Creator as one who
enormously transcends mortal man in His unimaginably
great qualities, but not one who has dissolved in a mys-
tical infinity unrelated to His children. Rather, we
worship the kind Father who knows His children and
loves them.

The Creator, an individual personage, in whose image
we are, nevertheless, has an influence which reaches
throughout space. This influence is exercised at least in
part through those who help Him. The modern concept
of the atom provides an interesting analogy. We can
perform experiments with x-rays which give the exact
dimensions of the atom. Yet if a column of atoms all
having the same velocity are directed against a solid
surface, they are reflected just like waves beating against
a walled enclosure. The atoms are thus surrounded by a
so-called electromagnetic field which extends out into
space beyond the limits of their substance. Atoms are
localized substance with measurable dimensions and yet
having an influence extending out into space.

It should be clear that there is a definite change in
the very nature of our thinking as we jump from the very
large to the infinite. This jump is a delicate one to make
in mathematics and has led to some very unhappy contradictions with theologians who have gone on their
own well beyond what God has revealed. Speculation is
only harmful as we confuse fact and fancy.

If one tosses a perfect coin, there is equal probability
that it will fall with either side up. If we represent by
p the chance that in a single throw we get heads and by
q the chance we get tails then $p + q = 1$. This is so
because if we throw it we must get either heads or tails.
If the coin is imperfect, so that p is less than $\frac{1}{2}$, say $\frac{1}{3}$.
then q must be $\frac{2}{3}$. Now if the coin is tossed twice, the
terms in the expression $(p + q)^2 = p^2 + 2pq + q^2$ give the

probabilities of the various things that can happen. Thus the chance that one gets heads both times is p^2 which is $\frac{1}{4}$ for a perfect coin. The chance that one time one gets heads and one time one gets tails is $2pq = \frac{1}{2}$; and the chance that both times one gets tails is $q^2 = \frac{1}{4}$. These results can easily be verified both by experiment and by a little thought. Now, if instead of throwing the coin twice one throws it n times the chance of the various things that can happen is given by the various terms in the expansions of $(p + q)^n$.

The theory of probability applies to the behavior of atoms and molecules in the world around us. Thus the whole world is continually moving toward states of greater and greater probability. It is a well known fact of experience that if we set a pot of boiling water on a table in a cool room the pot cools and when once cooled it never returns to the boiling point without outside heating. In just the same way the sun is forever giving off its heat and tending to grow colder. When it finally grows cold it can never grow hot again according to the scientific dogma known as the second law of thermodynamics.

According to this theory, when the sun ceases to shine all living things will die; all changes will cease and the world will have reached a deadly monotonous uniformity. This state is called the "heat death" and is a consequence of nature always moving toward more probable states and never in the reverse direction toward less probable states. This marvelously organized world is forever running down just like a fine watch which is not rewound. Eventually, according to science, the watch must stop. Such a picture gives a doubtful explanation of the end of things and no clue as to how the world was wound up in the first place, and scientists don't know the answer. Revealed writings give the Latter-day Saint many interesting facts about such matters. For instance, Isaiah, 65:17-25, Doctrine and Covenants 29: 22-25; 88:18-27.

An interesting calculation illustrates the complete improbability of a hot sun arising by chance. We suppose that in order again to become hot the sun must accumulate an amount of heat equal to that it gives off in its lifetime. This must be accumulated from its surroundings, which we shall assume in the heat death drop to a temperature of 700° Centigrade. Then using the straightforward theory of chemical reactions we find that a length of time in years equal to at least one with a hundred thousand, billion, billion, billion, billion, billion zeros must elapse before a hot sun has a "fifty-fifty" probability of occurring again by chance. This is almost no chance at all! Surely our hot sun did not arise by such a chance fluctuation. The Creator accomplishes His purposes by much more subtle means.

Finally it is interesting to ask who the best mathematicians have been and what were their religious attitudes. If one were to choose the three most famous mathematicians, probably the choice would be Archimedes, the Greek; Isaac Newton, the Englishman; and Carl Friederick Gauss, the German. Archimedes lived from 287-212 B.C. Of his religious ideas little is now known. Newton was an unquestioning believer in an allwise Creator of the universe. In fact, he made it his business to study and understand the creation. This great man devoted much of his time, especially after forty-five, to understanding the implications of the scriptures.

Gauss had this to say, "There are problems to whose solution I would attach an infinitely greater importance than to those of mathematics—for example, touching ethics, or our relation to God, or concerning our destiny and our future; but their solution lies wholly beyond us and completely outside the province of science."

We must find other reasons for being irreligious than the example of the elite of mathematics.

PART III

Truth in Science

Cosmic Design

L ATTER-DAY SAINTS ARE ENJOINED TO SEEK OUT ALL
useful knowledge. Years of association with university students makes it clear that an advisor's influence
is proportional to his general understanding of the
students' problems. For this reason, if for no other,
parents, teachers, and presiding authorities need to understand the problems confronting the rising generation.

All of us are tempted at times to give easy answers.
We are asked for bread and we give our questioner a
stone. This is usually because we just do not know the
correct answers. Scientific knowledge is piling up at such
an impressive rate that any comprehensive interpretation
of man's place in the universe requires a continuing
review of the relevant facts. We shall attempt here to
direct attention toward a few of the newer scientific
developments which require this re-interpretation.

Before 1920, high school students were routinely
taught that the elements were indestructible. The atomic
bomb spectacularly contradicts this age-old concept. In
the atomic bomb we have either uranium 235 or plu-
tonium breaking up into all the lighter elements with a
small part of the matter actually disappearing as it is
transformed into energy. The intense heat of the explosion is the visible result of this transformation. The
inverse process in which energy is changed into matter
has also been observed.

Thus, cosmic rays coming from outer space have
been observed in a cloud chamber to change over into
an electron and a positron. The positron has the same

mass but the opposite charge to the electron. The dog-
matist who may have built the indestructibility of matter
into some pet theory may be unhappy at this turn of
events, but the world really goes on much as it did
before. One has, in fact, only found out that matter and
energy are different forms of the same thing, and the
change that we had thought of as destruction is instead
a transformation of matter into energy. It is important
that this change takes place in both directions.

The scriptural description of spirit as a more refined
kind of matter takes on new perspective in the light of
this larger concept of the interchangeability of matter and
energy. Matter, in the broader sense, can still be spoken
of as indestructible, providing we realize that energy is
just another form of matter.

With this crumbling of our old ideas of the very
foundations of an indestructible world of matter, another
new concept has been born. Somewhere in space we
expect to find anti-worlds made from anti-matter. In all
outward respects anti-worlds look like ordinary worlds.
In fact an anti-world would be obtained from an ordinary
world by simply changing all positive charges to negative
and simultaneously changing all negative charges to positive. Thus, whereas atoms in the ordinary world have
positively charged nuclei with negatively charged electrons
circulating about them, the situation is exactly the reverse
in the anti-world. Here positively charged electrons,
called positrons, circulate about negatively charged
nuclei. In fact, if you could shed your material body and
pay a visit to either a world or an anti-world, it would
take some fairly fancy observing to tell which type of
world you were visiting. People would eat, sleep, and
live the same way. This ambiguity would disappear if
you kept your material body. The fireworks start whenever matter and anti-matter collide. Such a collision
would produce a ball of fire with the disappearance of
the smaller of the two colliding bodies together with an

equivalent amount of the other substance. The disappearing matter is transformed into energy giving the resulting super explosion. This explains why we do not see any anti-matter lying around loose near the earth. If there were some it would disappear as soon as encounters with matter occurred.

Two hundred million atoms touching each other in a line measure one inch. One hundred thousand atomic nuclei similarly arranged extend only across one atom. It is natural to wonder how anything as small as the nucleus can have structure, and even if it does have, how man can find it out. The procedure for finding out is to shoot electrically charged atoms or electrons at nuclei and see how they bounce. This tells us a great deal about the kind of forces that are acting between the colliding particles.

When a particularly violent collision results in penetration into the nucleus and causes it to fragment, we can watch the tracks left by the fragments in a cloud chamber. In this way we find out that the nucleus is made up of positively charged protons and uncharged neutrons of virtually the same weight. Now the question arises as to whether the nucleus has the same properties in all directions. The principle of parity which was accepted as true for 25 years states that an atom does not know one end from the other. It is interesting to see how this statement was proved to be untrue. Because the radioactive cobalt-60 nucleus is magnetic and so has a north and south pole, one can place a quantity of the cobalt in a magnetic field and have all the atomic nuclei line up with their south poles pointing toward the north pole of the big outside magnet. The nuclei stay lined up quite well if the cobalt is kept very cold. Now the cobalt nuclei are radioactive, and every once in a while one of them shoots out an electron. If the nuclei were indeed symmetrical they would be equally likely to eject the electron through their north pole as through the south pole. This is, however, not what happens. A geiger counter similar to those used to prospect for uranium reveals that the electrons are shot out preferentially through the nuclear south pole. Thus the principle of parity must be given up.

This ingenious experiment suggested by Yang and Lee, for which they were given the Nobel prize, has thus provided exciting new information about the structure of the nucleus.

Since we know of no sufficient reason why cobalt-60 should favor the ejection of particles along its south pole, it is natural to ask, "Where are the cobalt atoms which would eject particles along their north pole?" The probable answer is that in anti-matter the corresponding cobalt atoms will indeed be found to eject positrons along their north pole. It will not be easy to prove this surmise by direct observation.

Every piece of information of this kind reveals new facets of the cosmic design and increases our awe of the Supreme Intelligence operating through the universal reign of law. We turn next to an interesting aspect of the biological world.

Molecules are made by joining atoms together. A molecule resulting from such a combination of atoms is said to be symmetrical if one side of the molecule is the mirror image of the other side as, for example, one side of the body is a mirror image of the other side. Molecules which lack this symmetry are said to be asymmetric. Corresponding to every asymmetric molecule we have its mirror image which is called its "optical isomer." In the same way the left hand is the mirror image of the right hand.

The body is made up of many types of molecules, just as a large building may be made up of many types of bricks. Many of these molecules in the body are a-symmetrical, and frequently one optical isomer is found to occur in living things to the virtual exclusion of its mirror image. We can understand this selective choice of building blocks if we recognize that the body is built up by molecules which are to be incorporated into the body from the food we eat. This selection is made by a process of fitting of the selected molecule to the enzyme much as a left hand selects a left-hand glove and rejects a right-hand glove. Muscles and enzymes are made by joining amino acids together into long chains. These chains are called proteins. There are 20 different amino acids which are joined together in different proportions to form the links in the various types of protein chains. Of these 20 amino acids used by the body, all but one are asymmetric. Further, all the 19 asymmetric amino acids used are like the left hand glove and are called l-amino acids. In every living thing, the opposite optical isomers, which are called the d-amino acids, if present in the food, are rejected by the enzymes which build proteins and are eliminated from the body. We therefore call this world we live in an l-amino acid world. "L" comes from laevo, the latin word for left; and "d" stands for dextro or right.

We can readily imagine a d-amino acid world. In fact, if we look into a large mirror, the world we see is a d-amino world since every object, including the molecules, is the mirror image of those in the real world. Obviously everything in the d-amino acid world would work exactly as well as our real world, and it is a matter of no obvious consequence which world we happen to have. If there are other worlds which support life, there is no reason for supposing that they may not be d-amino acid worlds. If so, such worlds would be completely inhospitable to us since we could not digest their foods; and marriages between people coming from d and l worlds would necessarily be sterile. On the other hand, there is, of course, no reason why people from two such worlds might not converse with each other with complete understanding, and one could not tell the two types of people apart by their appearance.

The fact that in our world every living thing from the tiniest living cell to man uses only the l-amino acids along with the d-sugars highlights the unity running through the living world. Everything which grows, collects those particular optical isomers which man needs for his food and rejects the opposite isomers which are unfit for him to eat. Here again we catch a glimpse of that unity which everywhere characterizes the cosmic design.

Sir Isaac Newton three hundred years ago thought of light moving in straight lines and in general behaving much as material particles would. This point of view was given up when the Dutchman Hyghens showed that many experiments involving light were better understood if we thought of light as waves being deflected much as water waves are deflected by the obstructions on a pond. Still later, Maxwell developed the general theory of the wave nature of light to such a degree of perfection that the particle theory seemed completely discredited. The interesting point is that everyone felt that the particle theory and the wave theory of light were mutually exclusive. Light could be a particle or a wave, but it could not be both.

Then, in 1905, Albert Einstein published his theory of the photoelectric effect for which he was given the Nobel prize. If light hits a metal surface, electrons are ejected provided the light is violet enough in color. Further, the energy with which the electron is ejected is proportional to the frequency of the light and to nothing else. This can be understood if light is made up of particles with energy proportional to their frequency. Einstein called these light particles "photons," and with the acceptance of this particle theory, a full-blown paradox was born.

Physicists were at first thoroughly disturbed with this split personality exhibited by light, but as time went on they learned to live with it. It is now accepted that light is made up of the particle-like photons which, how-

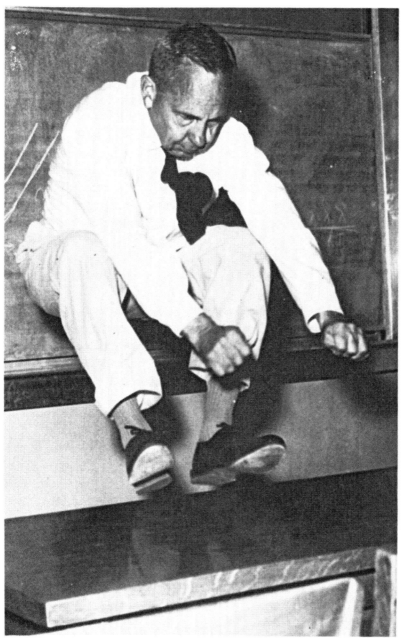

Henry Eyring still agile at 60, jumps on table from standing position.

ever, are accompanied by a wave which governs the direction in which light travels. On the other hand, whenever photons are absorbed by matter, they are swallowed up as a unit just as any other particle might be. If the physicists are not exactly happy with the schizophrenic nature of light, they have at least learned to live with it.

In the middle 1920's, DeBroglie predicted that particles of matter would be found to have waves associated with them, controlling their direction of travel just as light particles do. When a beam of electrons all having the same velocity is directed against a crystal, it is deflected just as light is. Accordingly, we must also think of matter as showing schizophrenic behavior, sometimes acting like a wave and sometimes like a particle. Again physicists have learned to live with the unexpected behavior.

If we read the story of Robert E. Lee, the great military tactician, we find that even at Gettysburg his army was maneuvered as though Lee were himself storming Cemetery Ridge alongside Pickett, as well as being everywhere else on the battlefield. Lee's success as a general depended to a very great extent on the gathering of information about the strength, position and intentions of his adversary before and after the battle started. The result is that any story of Lee as a general would tell about his influence permeating the whole sphere of his activities and very little about Lee the man. In this sense Lee is two people, the man like anyone else, and the farflung intelligence system which governed the motion of himself and his army much as the wave is spread out in space and governs the motion of a photon or a material particle.

In an analogous manner, we may think of God as the all-wise arbiter of the universe, with His infinite wisdom having an influence which permeates the most remote recesses of space, and yet being Himself an exalted being with personality and deep concern for struggling humanity. One of the many things the Restored Gospel has done is to emphasize, as the scriptures have always done, the deep personal concern of God for His children.

In this article we have barely touched the problems which confront the eager student, but perhaps in calling attention to the existence of such problems we may, in some degree, stimulate the never-ending quest for truth in all its varied forms.

Myriads of Worlds

THE EXPLORATION OF SPACE IS BRINGING CHANGES IN the world's thinking comparable only to the upheaval in thought which followed the voyages of Columbus.

First we were startled by Yuri Gagarin's passage into an orbit which circled the earth and returned him thrilled with the magnificent blue expanse which he had seen spread out beneath him. This Russian exploit was quickly followed by two American trips into space. This time we were virtually fellow passengers of the intrepid astronauts. Those who waited out the dragging hours before the take-off of Alan Shepard, as he rested on top of the giant missile which could at any moment become his funeral pyre, felt deep pride in his quiet courage and intense relief as he was lifted from the sea. Everything about this flight seemed to proceed according to plan— almost too perfectly.

On the late Virgil (Gus) Grissom's exciting first flight, the capsule was lost. The changes that the space program are bringing in transportation and in communication as well as the overall changes in our technology are incalculable. Grissom's first flight carried him to a height of 118 miles, and his Liberty Bell 7 speeded up to a maximum velocity of 5,310 miles per hour. Subsequent American unmanned flights have orbited the moon, landed on the moon and passed close to Mars and Venus.

What of the future? The late President John F. Kennedy set as the goal the placing of a man on the moon by 1970. This program is expected to cost in excess of 37 billion dollars. There are great perils attending such flights as was evidenced by the recent disaster which claimed the lives of Gus Grissom, Edward White and Roger Chaffee. During intense solar activity, bursts of particles from flares on the sun could cook the unhappy astronaut with the intense radiation. In the two Van Allen radiation belts above the earth's atmosphere, the radiation is too intense to allow people to remain in them; but swift passage through the belts by missiles seems feasible.

It is symptomatic of these changing times that the president of the United States should set as a goal this placing of a man on the moon within a short ten years. Since the moon is 241,000 miles away and since space travel might well proceed at up to a mean speed of 20,000 miles per hour, the journey would take around 12 hours. On the other hand, the sixty odd million miles to Venus would require about four months at this speed. Mars is a little closer and the other planets are still farther away. It takes the space traveler about 30,000 times as long as it takes for light to make the same journey.

The nearest neighboring solar system is so distant that light requires slightly over four years to make the transit. At our present rates of space travel, this journey would require 120,000 years. Consequently, we seem to be marooned in our solar system, at least for the time being. Present missile travel, which proceeds at a speed about a thousand times as fast as man can run, will need to be speeded up by another factor of a thousand before we can undertake trips beyond our solar system.

Even if we believe beings on distant planets have progressed far beyond us, still the barrier to travel posed by interstellar distances seems quite sufficient to explain why mortal space travelers have not visited us.

Professor Harlow Shapley, emeritus professor of

astronomy at Harvard University, has written an interesting book *Of Stars and Men*[1] in which he estimates that
there are a hundred million, million, million suns in
space. Now our sun has at least one planet—Earth—
which is suitable for life; and in addition, Mars and
Venus may support life. Shapley assumes that this may
not be true of all suns, but he very conservatively estimates that at least one sun in a thousand should have
acquired planets and that of those with planets, at least
one in a thousand has a planet at the right distance for
life.

Of those having a planet at the right distance, at
least one in a thousand should have a planet large enough
to hold an atmosphere and finally that one in a thousand
of those having a large enough planet at the right distance should have an atmosphere of the right composition
to support life. Thus one concludes that there should be
at the very minimum one hundred million planets in
space which could support life, and the number is probably many times more. From the scientific point of
view, it is hard to doubt that there are myriads of
worlds suitable for human habitation.

As exciting as this modern information is, and as
closely as it seems to parallel our religious thinking, still
the fact remains that the problems of where we came
from, where we are going, and the purpose of it all must
ultimately be answered from the divine source open to
Abraham and to all men—and from this source only.

The mysteries of the universe lead most men to
worship the Supreme Intelligence who designed it all.
However, the great blessing of the Gospel is the additional
avenues it opens up for developing this faith into a perfect knowledge. Now, as always, sure knowledge of
spiritual matters can only come by faith, by prayer and
by living in such a way as to have the companionship
of the Holy Ghost as is promised to all the faithful.

---

[1]Harlow Shapley, *Of Stars and Men*, 1960 edition; Washington Square Press,
Inc., New York; pages 48-68.

The Gospel and the Age
of the Earth

R ECORDED HISTORY SPANS SCARCELY A MOMENT OUT OF
eternity. The scriptures record God's dealing with
His children back to a "beginning" some six thousand
years ago, but dismiss the long prologue in a few short
paragraphs. The scriptural information which is given
to us concentrates on the accepted plan for our earthly
pilgrimage and unfolds a program of eternal progression
in the life to come. This unfolding of limitless possibilities
extends backward in time into pre-earth life.

What about the earth itself? The scriptures tell us of
six creative periods followed by a period of rest. During
these periods the earth was organized and took essentially
its present form. The accounts of creation in modern
scripture serve to corroborate the biblical account. In
the King James version of the Bible, the phrase "creative
periods" is rendered as "days." The use of this term has
led to at least three interpretations. In the first, the days
are construed to mean the usual day of 24 hours. In the
second the days of creation are interpreted as thousand-
year periods following such statements as occur in II
Peter 3:8: ". . . one day is with the Lord as a thousand
years, and a thousand years as one day." The third
interpretation accepts "creative periods" as times of
unspecified length and looks to a study of the earth itself
to give added meaning to the exceedingly brief scriptural
accounts.

The acceptance of truth, from whatever source, is

the constant goal of the thoughtful Latter-day Saint.
Since God organized the world, there can be no contradictions in His mind. Our problem is to approach His
deeper insight. As this is achieved, all the seeming
contradictions may be expected to disappear.

In earlier times some variation of the first two
interpretations was all but universally held by the Christian world. This is no longer true. In school and in
secular publications the third interpretation is the generally accepted one. Accordingly, whatever our own
point of view may be, we need to know the viewpoint
presented to our children if we are to be effective coun-
selors to them.

Every process occurring in the world requires time to
execute it and is necessarily of shorter duration than the
life span of the earth. The giant sequoias growing in
California are known to live 3,000 years from a count of
their tree rings. Accordingly, the earth is more than
3,000 years old. Interestingly enough, the sequoias are
not the oldest known trees. The bristle-cone pine, which
is found in parts of California, Nevada and Utah, has
yielded a specimen which is at least 4,600 years old. This
is more than a third of the 13 millennia sometimes taken
as the age of the earth. A late figure for the cumulative
thickness of rocks laid down as sediments is about
450,000 feet or about 80 miles. The rate of deposition
varies enormously with the time and the place, but a not
unreasonable average rate is one foot every 250 years.
This leads to a very rough estimate of 112,000,000 years
for the time required to deposit all the known sediments.

The fact that a tree can stand in one spot more than
four thousand years without being seriously disturbed by
erosion leads one to contemplate with awe the thousands
of years required to deposit the strata of the Grand
Canyon and afterwards to erode these strata away.

A more quantitative way of getting at the age of
strata and of other earth structures is by use of the radio-

active decay of various elements. An analogy illustrative of how radioactive decay works may be helpful. If one should look at a fire and note that half the wood is burned the first hour and an hour later that half of the remainder has burned to ashes, one could say the fire obeys the radioactive decay law. This law states that in a given length of time the same fraction of the fuel is transformed independent of the circumstances. Conversely, by measuring the fuel remaining at a fire and the amount of ashes produced, one can deduce the fraction of the fuel consumed and so estimate how long the fire has been burning.

All the radioactive elements behave like our hypothetical fire in that, independent of the existing conditions, the same fraction of the radioactive elements is always transformed to the daughter element in a given interval of time. The daughter element is the ashes of the radioactive fire; for example, half of the potassium, of atomic weight forty, present to begin with changes into argon forty in a period of 1,300 million years, and half of what remains is changed in the next 1,300 million years. This period of 1,300 million years is called the half-life of potassium forty.

A potassium-containing mineral when it crystallizes is ordinarily freed of all gaseous argon. As time goes on, the potassium forty changes over to argon forty at a rate determined by its half-life. If the crystal doesn't leak so that the liberated argon is retained inside the crystal, one can melt the crystal, measure the amount of potassium and the amount of argon, and so determine the age of the crystal.

If equal amounts of argon forty and potassium forty are found, the crystallization occurred 1,300 million years ago. If only one quarter of the potassium remains, 2,600 million years have elapsed since crystallization of the mineral occurred, and so on. Clearly, any potassium-containing mineral constitutes a built-in clock which we can use to read the time of the formation of the crystalline mineral.

Many complications may arise to make the clock give incorrect time. If some argon were entrapped in the crystal as it formed, the clock will read too long a time. If some of the argon has escaped since crystallization occurred, the indicated time will be too short. Nonetheless, by being careful to choose elements with appropriate half-lives and by careful selection of the crystal used and by frequent cross checking, that is by using more than one clock, a reasonably consistent time scale for the formation of the various strata in the world has been achieved.

According to radioactive dating, the oldest fossil-bearing rocks, called lower Cambrian, are about 600 million years old, and geologists find that life has existed continuously as shown by the fossils found in the successive layers of sediments deposited since Cambrian time.

The earliest life found in the Cambrian strata was very simple in form and increased in complexity with the years, according to the fossil record. Eventually, that is, about 100 million years ago, the monstrous dinosaurs walked the earth only to disappear in their turn as new forms of life, better adapted to changing conditions, displaced them.

Most scientists using this and other kinds of evidence agree on an age for the earth of about four and one-half billion years. On the other hand, the exact age of the earth is apparently of so little import religiously that the scriptures sketch earth history only in the briefest terms. The present heated religious controversies on the subject will undoubtedly be resolved in time and will then appear as quaint as the medieval arguments on the shape of the earth seem to us now.

Gospel truths which influence our salvation are unaffected by considerations such as this. For instance, since the fall made man subject to death, it comes to every son of Adam who receives a mortal body. Since the Atonement is to overcome death, then ". . . as in Adam all men die, even so in Christ shall all be made alive" (1 Corinthians 15:22) is also equally true whatever the age of the earth. The Gospel of Christ will be lighting the world long after this and other knotty problems cease to agitate us.

SUGGESTED SUPPLEMENTARY READING

1. Brigham Young, *Journal of Discourses*, Vol. 14, p. 115.
2. James E. Talmage, "The Earth and Man," *Deseret News*, November 21, 1931.
3. Scriptures on time: Book of Abraham, p. 35, Fig. 1; 3:4, 5:13; D&C 88:44; 77:6; Alma 40:8; Helaman 8:18; Psalm 90:4; 2 Peter 3:8.
4. John A. Widtsoe, The Improvement Era, Vol. 41, p. 713.
5. William Lee Stokes, *Essentials of Earth History* (Englewood Cliffs, N.J.; Prentice-Hall, Inc., 1960), Ch. 2.
6. Arthur Holmes, "A Revised Geological Time Scale," *Trans. Edinburgh Geological Society*, Vol. 17 (1959), part 3, pp. 183-216.
7. J.A.S. Adams and J.J.W. Rogers, "Bentonites as Absolute Time Stratigraphic Calibration Points," *Annals of the New York Academy of Science*, Vol. 91 (1961), p. 390.
8. G.W. Wetherill, "Radioactivity of Potassium and Geologic Time," *Science*, Vol. 126 (1957), No. 3273, p. 545.
9. Lawrence Kulp, "Geologic Time Scale," *Science*, Vol. 133 (1961), No. 3459, p. 1105.

PART IV

Truth in Religion

The Religious Faith of
a Chemist

IT IS NATURAL FOR ME TO WORSHIP THE SUPREME INTEL-ligence of the universe. This Supreme Intelligence necessarily exists since the world is full of unequally intelligent beings. Harlow Shapley estimates there are some 10^{20} suns having companion satellites analogous to our earth. Most of these satellites are at such distances from their suns that they are either too hot or too cold to support life as we know it. Still others lack life-giving water, while others lack the necessary oxygen. However, after guessing that at least one in every 10^{12} of these planets should be uninhabitable, Professor Shapley is left with at least 10^8, or 100,000,000 planets on which it is reasonable to suppose that life could and does exist. (Harlow Shapley, *Of Stars and Men;* Beacon Press, Beacon Hill, Boston, 1958; page 74 and following.)

It is accordingly natural to conclude that the universe is flooded with intelligent beings and, presumably, always has been. Any unfolding of intelligences that may eventuate on this earth only repeats what has happened previously elsewhere. The biblical account of an all-wise Providence shaping human destiny is a natural expectation for me, and this belief is shared by a large fraction of mankind.

The fact that we are alive disposes of the many weighty arguments that might otherwise be adduced to prove that human life in all its complexity could not exist. Also, the wonder of being born into this world makes one discount arguments that rule out our rebirth into immortality on the ground that it would be too complex. An argument of excessive complexity in effect supposes that the Supreme Intelligence could not work such wonders since the doubter would be hard pressed himself to do it.

Another argument sometimes directed against religious beliefs is that as man's knowledge grows, his reasons for being religious disappear along with his other ill-founded superstitions. Instead, I believe that every brilliant conquest made by man is but a manifestation of the divine spark which sets him apart from the rest of creation. Man is in the image of God, destined to go on learning and perfecting himself throughout eternity. To accept the idea that the human personality ends with death is to accept life as a futile, meaningless gesture. God would be less compassionate than many good men if life ended at the grave. Broken, uncompleted lives are the best possible reason for a hereafter in which the scales of justice are balanced by a just God. To believe otherwise is to attribute to God a lack of the sensitivity that we find regularly in good men. Such a supposition is incredible to me.

For one who feels compelled, as I do, to accept the existence of the Master Architect, it is important to examine His handiwork for the light it throws on Him and on His program for His children.

Man has perfected the art of communication to the point where he can direct a satellite to photograph Mars and later have it relay the picture back to earth. There seems to be virtually no limit to man's possibilities of communication and of space exploration. Considering such human achievements, it is reasonable to suppose that the only limitations God places on His communications with man are those which are necessary to best carry out His divine purposes. Accordingly, I am led to accept revealed religion as something which is to be expected.

Since the Bible gives the best available account of God's dealings with man in ancient times, I find it natural to accept it as the prophetic record of these events. But since the Bible has passed through human hands, it is inevitable that it should reflect human fallibility as well as divine inspiration. It should be accepted for what it is—a divine message of inspiration and hope to struggling humanity. It outlines the divine plan by which man may return to his immortal state where he may grow endlessly in wisdom and in understanding of the mysteries that are at present veiled to him. Since the need for prophetic guidance still exists, I find it natural to believe it is still present in the contemporary world and so I accept as modern scripture the prophetic writings of today. All prophetic insights, recorded and spoken, give the believer consolation as well as encouragement to live the good life that eventually will be weighed in the balance at a final judgment.

Apparent contradictions between religion and science often have been the basis of bitter controversy. Such differences are to be expected as long as human understanding remains provisional and fragmentary. Only as one's understanding approaches the Divine will all seeming contradictions disappear. Such complete understanding is to be approached as a part of the eternal progress which will continue in the life to come. In the meantime, we can only continue our quest for the balanced view that comes from weighing all evidence carefully in the search for enduring values. The road is a long one, but the outcome is assured if we are willing to travel it.

Man continually searches for a simple, unified picture of the most complex phenomena. He is not always successful in his quest. Newton conceived of light as particles moving in straight lines, i.e., as rays. Later Hyghens was able to show that the diffraction of light could be understood only if one thought of light as waves which, when they become reflected from obstacles, set up interference patterns like the waves one sees reflected from obstacles on the surface of a pond of water. The wave theory was so successful in explaining diffraction of light that the Newtonian particle view was completely discredited for many years.

However, in 1905 Einstein explained the observed ejection of electrons from metals by light as due to the absorbed photons, or light particles colliding with the electrons. The energy, E, of the photons obeys the Einstein relation $E = h v$ where v is the frequency of light and h is Planck's constant. The wave-particle behavior of light is also paralleled by the wave-particle nature of material particles. The concept that material particles are governed by a wave which is associated with them is the basis for modern wave mechanics.

Something like this dualism exists with respect to the concepts of God. The scriptures picture Him as an exalted Being, while some later interpretations dwell on the fact that His influence fills the universe. Rather than being contradictory, these are probably best thought of as two aspects of the same exalted being. The influence of even a great earthly ruler may extend to every corner of his realm. This powerful influence, however, is quite properly not confused with the person of the earthly ruler. In an analogous fashion, God may be thought of as more than the great influence which He exerts upon the world.

If the human spirit exists prior to birth and again afterwards, as I believe, one must distinguish between this eternal spirit and the body with which it is united in mortality. This duality disturbs some minds, but we have had to learn to live with such pluralism when contemplating light and matter. One might wish the world were simpler, but that will hardly make it so. Certain problems are at least placed in a different perspective if we think of pre-mortal and post-mortal existence. We may then suppose that our situation in this life may have been conditioned by what took place in our pre-mortal state, in the same way that we expect our actions here to affect the life to come.

The purpose of living is to grow in wisdom and goodness, and this growth is possible only because God gives man freedom to choose. This freedom necessarily gives man the opportunity to make wrong choices as well as right ones. But choosing the wrong course is a sin. The degree of culpability of a person who sins depends on the gravity of the error and his opportunities for avoiding it. Our opportunity to grow would cease if freedom of choice were withheld. However, the banishing of error while still preserving freedom to choose will be the inevitable consequence of an increase in understanding and in goodwill. It is reasonable, therefore, to look forward to a free society in which sin will have all but disappeared.

I think of our birth as the clothing of an immortal spirit in an earthly body. By being born into the world, each individual becomes subject to death. This constitutes the Fall of man. Since he is to live again after death with an immortal body, the resurrection comes as a gift to mortals from the Savior of mankind. This gift was made possible by the Atonement.

To argue that life cannot be created is to argue that life has always existed, for it now exists. To the degree that man is able consciously to contribute to the organization that is necessary for life, to that degree he demonstrates the divine spark which sets him apart from the rest of nature. How far he may ultimately go in this direction, presumably, depends on how well he can master the intricate principles involved. For me it is necessary to support the thesis that all of nature is subject to God's will. Experience indicates, however, that as scientists the depth of our understanding sets the limits to which we can influence natural phenomena. It is unreasonable to suppose that God feels threatened by the puny scientific accomplishments of His children. In this spirit I find in each human triumph additional reason to believe in man's exalted destiny and that he is important enough to merit and receive divine justice.

Science deals only with *how* the world works and has little to say about *why* the world is as it is. Values, also, are something apart from science. We must find the meaning of life in religion and in metaphysics. Even if by breaking the genetic code, for example, we should learn how to change human inheritance and so affect human destiny, the meaning of life would remain as tantalizing a question as it was before. If we think of the universe as analogous to a great machine, then man is learning through science something about how the machine works, but only through philosophy and religion can he catch a glimpse of the purposes of the Designer and His reasons for the grand design. Many of the burning questions which are the substance of human hopes and fears are answered by religion for the believer.

Chemistry is the science of the behavior of aggregates of atoms and molecules and as such underlies all the material sciences. Studying it, we conclude that chemical laws follow from wave mechanics and the coulomb law of attraction between electrons and positively charged nuclei. Learning this and implementing it is science. The existence of such amazing unity and simplicity of design brings a sense of awe inspired only by an artistic masterpiece. With this comes once again an acute awareness of the Master Designer.

Faith in God

THE MORE I TRY TO UNRAVEL THE MYSTERIES OF THE world in which we live, the more I come to the conception of a single overruling power—God. One can come to this point of view by prayer and the testimony of the Holy Ghost or because there seems to be no other explanation of the unity and wonder of the universe or by the pragmatic method of science that the Savior suggested long ago—try it and you will know.

I have often met this question: "Dr. Eyring, as a scientist, how can you accept revealed religion?" The answer is simple. The Gospel commits us only to the truth. The same pragmatic tests that apply in science apply to religion. Try it. Does it work? The conception of a God ruling the universe and concerned with how it works is impossible for me without the corollary that He should be interested in man, the most remarkable phenomenon in the world. Being interested in man, it is natural that He would provide a plan for man's development and welfare. This plan is the Gospel of Jesus Christ.

This immediately raises many questions. At best, men are faltering and imperfect. The Savior stands alone as the perfect example. The Gospel is indeed the plan which the Creator of the universe has devised to guide His children and bring them back to Him. Through the ages, He has chosen from among His worthy sons prophets to act as guides to His children. Today, the Church of Jesus Christ of Latter-day Saints is presided over by good and wise men who instruct and counsel those who have the wisdom to listen.

In the great council of the premortal life, a tremendous decision was made that man was to have his free agency. This brings with it many interesting problems, since the Lord's children often make unwise decisions with tragic results. War and catastrophe are taken by some people to be evidence against the existence of a God, or at least His unconcern for the evils that overtake man. I think this should be thought of in a completely different light.

Lucifer promised to bring salvation to every soul, whether the person to be saved desired it or not. Dictators have been operating in the same way from time immemorial. Never has there been a more concerted effort to take away free agency than in the modern communistic world where about one per cent of the population rules through force and terror. God's non-intervention in human affairs is not a sign of His absence or His disinterest. Rather, it exemplifies one of His greatest gifts—free agency, which enables us to work out our individual salvation. If Lucifer were ruling the world, no one could doubt his presence.

There is a related argument that interests me. One sees good people cut off by death in their prime. This seems to me to be evidence for a life after death. It is impossible to reconcile such incompleteness with any other idea than that we will live again and that what we have lost through no fault of our own will be made up to us in full by a just God.

The wonderful Gospel plan as advocated by the Savior in the pre-existence, known by His prophets down through the ages and announced by Him personally during His earthly ministry, has again been restored by the Prophet Joseph Smith, working as an instrument of the Father. With it we have a rational understanding of life. Eternal progression as a result of wise choices through the use of free agency gives the complete and satisfying explanation of the world in which we live and the struggles we are called upon to make. The success of man in sending satellites into space is arresting evidence of the great capabilities of and the destiny of man, the spirit child of God.

I, as a mere man, instruct others. I am dedicated as a scientist and the significant thing about a scientist is this: he simply expects the truth to prevail because it *IS* the truth. He doesn't work very much on the reactions of the heart. In science, the thing *IS*, and its being so is something one cannot resent. If a thing is wrong, nothing can save it, and if it is right, it cannot help succeeding.

So it is with the Gospel. I had the privilege of serving with four other Church members in a conference in which, as a group, we undertook to answer the questions the assembled young folk might ask us.

One of the questions was addressed directly to me. A young man said: "In high school we are taught such things as pre-Adamic men, and that kind of thing, but we hear another thing in Church. What should I do about it?"

I think I gave the right answer. I said, "In this Church, you only have to believe the truth. Find out what the truth is!"

If there is anyone else who is trying to teach anything else with authority, this Church is not the least worried about that question or any other kind of question, because the Church is committed only to the truth. I do not mean to say that as individuals in the Church each one always knows the actual truth, but we have the humility sometimes to say we do not know the answers to these things. No Latter-day Saint needs to worry about any question of that kind because the Church is committed to the truth.

Some have asked me: "Is there any conflict between science and religion?" There is no conflict in the mind of God, but often there is conflict in the minds of men. Through the eternities, we are going to get closer and closer to understanding the mind of God, then the conflicts will disappear.

In the great council in heaven, already referred to, two plans were offered—one whereby the minds of men would be compelled to accept the truth. There would be no choice. Man would make no error. The other plan was set forth by God. In His plan, man would have his free agency. He could decide between the Church of God and all other ways of operating in the world.

God rules from heaven. He does it with such silken threads that some think he has lost the reins. Some people do not even know that He exists. Others wonder whether He exists. I have often thought that a condition like this could never have come about if a dictator such as Hitler or Stalin were ruling.

God is so gentle, so dedicated to the principle that men should be taught correct principles and then govern themselves, that they should take responsibility for their own mistakes, that His children can actually question whether He exists. To me, that in itself is one of the testimonies that He exists. I cannot think of anything which more wonderfully typifies His mercy, His kindness, His consideration for us, His concern for us, than that He does it all with bonds that are like strongest steel but are so gentle that you cannot see them.

I do know that He exists. It *IS* true, as great men have known throughout the ages, that this great world we live in is governed by powers more powerful than those of the world. I ask you to look at the wisest man you know and ask yourself whether you believe he is the greatest intellect in the universe. Do you think the tremendous order and wonderful things that have come into the world were created by something with no more understanding than this wise man you know? Of course you do not. It is unthinkable.

I worship the Supreme Intelligence of the universe, and I am convinced that, wise as men are and in spite of the wonderful things they have done, the Creator of this universe goes so far beyond anything that men understand that it is ridiculous to talk of the two in the same terms. So far as I have been able to observe, those who study deeply into scientific matters are often of that persuasion.

The Prophet Joseph Smith was indeed the inspired instrument in restoring the Gospel of the Savior, as is shown by the way it works in the lives of men. Since all truth has a single source, the apparent conflicts that often trouble us reflect only our incomplete understanding and must eventually be happily resolved. Eternal progress is man's destiny.

In Search of Truth

THERE IS AN URGENCY ABOUT THE SEARCH FOR TRUTH in this crisis-ridden world that has rarely existed before. Should we fail, our way of life could vanish. It is important to consider what our problems are and how we must meet them.

That the God-given principles of the Gospel prescribe the only cure to the present ills of the world does not alter the fact that the Gospel will be completely ineffectual if these principles are not accepted. Consequently, each of us has two main tasks. *First,* to know what these principles are and to follow them. *Second,* to do all within our power to see that the rest of the world understands these principles and also practices them.

No more august occasion is possible for the emergence of the first of these great principles than the council which involved the acceptance of free agency. This plan became the charter to which free men subscribed for the privilege of coming to earth and continuing their eternal progression. This was the auspicious beginning for the Gospel plan. Sometimes well-meaning people mistakenly describe dictators as those "wanting to play God." Nothing could be further from the truth. Instead, insofar as they exercise unrighteous dominion, they are anti-Christ.

Latter-day Saints are cautioned in these words:

> . . . When we undertake to cover our sins, or to gratify our pride, our vain ambition, or to exercise control or dominion or compulsion upon the souls of the children of men, in any degree of unrighteousness, behold, the heavens withdraw themselves; . . . (Doctrine and Covenants 121:37.)

*Henry Eyring receives the University Alumni Award. Dean
Sterling M. McMurrin, Henry Eyring and President A.
Ray Olpin, 1961.*

Again, when the Prophet Joseph Smith was asked how he managed to govern the Saints in Nauvoo so well, he answered, "I teach them correct principles and they govern themselves." President Dwight D. Eisenhower highlighted this same problem by challenging the Communists to United Nations-sponsored free elections in which to choose between their present form of government and a democratic system like that of the United States. Indeed, the cold war, with the ever-present threat of becoming hot, hangs over the world today because dictators seek to deny to their fellow men the divine right of free agency. This is the troubled world in which we live with its challenge to all we value most. What should we do about it?

In the spring of 1960, I lectured at Haverford, a Quaker college near Philadelphia, Pennsylvania, and was asked the inevitable question, "What is the position of your Church with respect to war?" The answer was easy. Like the Quakers, we are against war. The problem is how to prevent it.

The ultimate solution to the problem is to teach the Gospel to the whole world and to have it accepted. Nothing less will really resolve our difficulties. In the meantime, it is not likely that our country will be attacked if we are excellent enough in our character, in our science and engineering, in our economy and in our armaments. This puts the challenge back where it belongs—to each of us to reach the highest potential of which he is capable. Anything less could spell disaster.

Already great scientific advances have grown as a result of our necessity—the atomic bomb, atomic power, radioactive medicine, enormous advances in understanding nuclear structure, great advances in radioactive dating, and now satellites. The electronic devices that control the satellites and operate the giant calculators are not less wonderful. In communication systems, radio and television seem wonderful enough, but radar is being extended to new wave lengths so that astonomers are now observing stellar bodies which were not even known to exist a few years ago.

Secrets of chemical structure are likewise being revealed by microwaves, which are radar waves in the neighborhood of an inch long. This is about 100,000 times the wave length of visible light. With these microwaves, the turning wrong side out of the ammonia molecule, which occurs 24,000,000,000 times a second, can be measured with fabulous precision. The radar circuit can be tuned to the frequency of vibrations of various molecules or atoms to give a clock of previously unimagined accuracy.

We have read of the giant missile, Polaris, launched from our atomic submarines 40 feet below the surface of the sea. It sped 1,200 miles to strike directly on target. Every nation in the world is now on every other nation's frontier. The English Channel and the widest ocean are as archaic as a castle moat as defenses against Polaris. These are a few of the things we have done. We may be sure our adversaries have also been busy.

There is literally no end to such scientific truths and devices. But, unfortunately, possessing them does not solve our problems. We dare not slacken our pace until a world order is somehow achieved which recognizes and preserves the rights of the individual soul. The world is truly girding for Armageddon. Only if man recognizes the dilemma and matures spiritually can we avert disaster. This has long been foretold in the scriptures. Now even the most dull must see it.

But this is no time for despair. It is our great opportunity. If we and enough others continue unfalteringly in search of truth in all fields and live as the Gospel teaches, threatening as the future seems, we will ride out the storm. However, nothing but our best is good enough.

Obedience is the Price
of Freedom

THE TITLE OF THIS ARTICLE IS PARADOXICAL. IF ONE IS tied down by rules, how can he be free? For a school teacher there are duties that must be performed, or else he must find another job. Long ago I learned how to win freedom from my regular responsibilities: by fulfilling those duties over and beyond what is required. Here, certainly, obedience is the price of freedom.

If one breaks the law of the land, he soon learns that ignorance of the law is no excuse. Ideally at least, retribution is swift and sure. Yet for one who lives above the law, obeying it faithfully, there is complete freedom from all legal strictures; and the law becomes a protecting shield against every illegal invasion of one's rights by others.

Natural law likewise exacts strict obedience. One who takes a deadly poison must suffer the consequences, if nothing is done to protect him, whether or not those consequences seem appropriate. Ignorance of natural law is no excuse. Man is learning to shape the world to serve his needs in a way never before imagined. The miracle of launching a satellite and directing it to land on the moon or to pass by Mars and photograph the surface and afterwards relay the pictures back to earth is a triumph of painstaking and detailed obedience to natural law. A single mistake can completely nullify the results of years of the most exacting labors. Natural law is a hard master. One can succeed in implementing a choice he makes only by most careful obedience to the laws on which the choice is predicated. The aspiring scientist can learn no other lesson that will serve him so well as that of yielding the strictest compliance to every detail of natural law. In no other way can he probe the mysteries of the world around him.

In the spiritual realm, we learn from revelation that the attainment of any blessing is predicated upon obedience to the laws which govern that blessing. The Prophet Joseph Smith was surpassed by some in secular learning, but he was unsurpassed by anyone in his humble willingness to learn. He was genuinely teachable and was always willing to yield obedience to the promptings of the Spirit. The result was a God-given insight into spiritual matters that is having its effect for good throughout the world.

By yielding obedience to correct principles, the Prophet became one of the great leaders of all time. His followers are willing to follow him in a course which they recognize transcends all others in importance. Such a leader, with a great cause to which he and his followers can completely dedicate themselves, changes the world. Obedience to Gospel principles can make man master of himself, and thus of his own destiny. There is no greater freedom than this. Obedience to the laws of health, including the Word of Wisdom, frees man from the restrictions that come from bodily ills.

Nephi, when he was charged with obtaining the plates from Laban, said to his father:

> . . . I will go and do the things which the Lord hath commanded, for I know that the Lord giveth no commandments unto the children of men, save he shall prepare a way for them that they may accomplish the thing which he commandeth them. (1 Nephi 3:7.)

This assurance, and the freedom from worry that comes to the believer through obedience to the commandments, is a great source of strength that cannot be equalled. Nothing is in sharper contrast to Nephi's peace of mind than the haunting misery of the transgressor, unable to repent, caught in a web of his own making from which he is unable to escape.

The faithful Latter-day Saint who has been taught to accept the calls that come to him through proper channels and who discharges these responsibilities faithfully has access to the inner ". . . peace of God, which passeth all understanding. . . ." There is no greater gift than this.

Finally, almost every member of the Church is called to positions of leadership where, if he is to succeed, he must enlist the support of others. Only as he operates in obedience to Gospel principles can he expect the human and the divine support he must have to succeed. In the 121st Section of the Doctrine and Covenants, beginning at verse 34, members of the priesthood are instructed in the principles that must be followed if they are to effectively use this priesthood. It is good advice for all others. Nothing of importance is ever accomplished by man except by obedience to correct principles. Obedience is, in very deed, the price of freedom.

Why be a Latter-day Saint?

THE WORLD MAY BE LIKENED TO A GREAT BUILDING filled with people who are unable to reach the windows high above the floor unless they are willing to make an almost superhuman effort. At one end is the one-way entrance. Here we see the infants enter, mature, labor, and grow old, and most of them never make the struggle to reach the windows where they could catch a glimpse of the otherwise invisible world that surrounds them. Instead, they talk with each other, and not finding anyone who has actually looked through the windows, they decide that probably there aren't any after all and that the stories handed down of great men who by their struggle have glimpsed a world beyond are the inventions of knaves or fools.

In spite of this doubt, however, the stories live on. Some of them tell of prophets who have struggled to a window and actually talked a few moments to the kind Father who created it all. He is very busy with His other children who have already come from this and the other buildings into the garden. He smiles at His brave sons and gives them words of encouragement to take back to His other children. He tells them how to organize a school to prepare them for the life to come.

Some of the prophets, in their anxiety to help their brothers, place a mirror at the window to reflect the vision they have seen, hoping thereby to encourage the faltering ones. This mirror, which is the prophet's mind, reflects rays fashioned of the spoken or written word, and the result is at best imperfect. In the most favorable case the reflection is a blurred and indistinct image of the momentous reality.

The image is caught again by some one of us on the mental mirror which is our mind and after a second distortion we catch a glimpse of another world. No wonder one finds seeming flaws and inconsistencies. After a few centuries words themselves change their meaning; but more serious still, the prophet can use only words and ideas which both he and his hearers understand, if the image is to be perceived.

These words or ideas may be likened to the various colors of the spectrum. At best we see only a narrow band of the spectrum, and some of us, by our carelessness and neglect, are color-blind, so that try as we will our faulty mirror tells us almost nothing of the spiritual world. In our annoyance or arrogance we assume every mirror to be as faulty as our own.

The result is that in the building many schools have been set up. Some schools accept one leader and some another, and some are badly misled by ambitious and self-interested men. There is one surprising characteristic of most of these schools, or churches, which seems to me to disqualify them for people who want to go properly prepared into the garden. It is this: In spite of the changes in the experience and habits of thinking and even in the very language of men, these schools say we need no more vision. They say men used to climb to the windows and look out into the garden and get inspirations and instructions for themselves and their fellows but that all this has been changed. About two thousand years ago the kind Father decided we needed no further instruction, and so He drew the blinds and left us to our own devices and to our incomplete records of the visions of the past.

But there is at least one school which believes that

its great men can still climb to the window and get
necessary instruction—that the curtains have not been
drawn. I am thankful to a kind Providence that I've
been allowed to go to that school. This is one very
important reason for being a Latter-day Saint. When
the silent and inevitable messenger calls us into the
garden, let us not go unprepared.

PART V

Influencing Others With
Religious Truth

Gospel Teaching I Remember Best

THERE IS NO GREATER BLESSING THAN TO BE BORN INTO a happy Latter-day Saint home. From my earliest memory loyalty to the Gospel and loyalty to truth have been considered synonymous. I first remember my father saying something that I've often heard since—"One can risk only the truth with untrained missionaries."

I never cease being thankful for the absence in Gospel teaching of "the party line" which conspirators have always found indispensable since the time when Lucifer first proposed the abrogation of free agency down to the latest ruthless dictatorships which have swallowed up most of Asia and Eastern Europe. In contrast, the Lord's Church can entrust the truth to lay teachers and to a lay clergy.

I was taught early that the Gospel, being true, is priceless, but also that because it is true it is immensely sturdy—not fragile.

From Caroline Romney Eyring, my mother, I learned many Gospel truths. I cannot remember when I first heard her say, "Don't just be good, be good for something." Her life exemplified this saying to the last heroic breath. Her last illness with cancer of the stomach was a time of pleasant visiting with her children and friends —the first opportunity she had found to rest in a busy life of homemaking, Relief Society presiding and Sunday School teaching. She died at 80, an active member of the St. Joseph Stake Sunday School board.

By my wife, Mildred Bennion Eyring, our three sons and I have been schooled in uncompromising integrity— "Tithing is one-tenth." One doesn't easily forget testimonies lived in the home.

I cannot begin to list the wonderful Gospel teachers I remember. High on my list is my second intermediate teacher in Pima, Fred G. Webb. Pleasant, intelligent and successful businessman that he was, he took the time to teach the Gospel to his son, Max, and to the rest of us.

Today in Monument Park Ward I regret each appointment that keeps me away from three wonderful teachers. Successful John Simonsen, teacher of the high priests in the ward, quips over a mountain of references and sells the Gospel positively—the way he believes it. College professor, Ewart Swinyard, with the scholarliness typical of a top pharmacologist, humbly presents "Gospel Doctrine." Lawyer W. Eldredge Grant, Jr., makes the study of genealogy a vital, exciting experience with just the right amount of good humor.

Finally, steeped in the sciences as I am, I can always turn to the teachings of Orson Pratt, James E. Talmage, or John A. Widtsoe and get just the right slant on the Gospel for scientific friends—young and old. The divine Gospel is unchanging, but it is wonderfully presented anew in our generation.

Keys to Growth

"THE LESSONS THIS YEAR ARE JUST NOT SUITABLE FOR me to teach. I don't like them. I hate to ask to be released but I feel I must."

Superintendents sometimes have to answer this argument. Have you wanted to quit your teaching job and then gone back to your task with firm determination to see it through? If you have, you have discovered what we all discover sooner or later. Great triumphs grow out of near defeats. The load that is a little too heavy doesn't crush you as you knew it would. The added strength to bear the burden comes from somewhere.

Abraham Lincoln, crude, uncouth, not particularly religious, disposed of his household goods to acquire the means to move into the White House. His was a giant's task. The nation was on the verge of disaster. The cynics smiled at and resented this backwoodsman in the White House. War came. He was surrounded by proud, ambitious men, some of whom were much less than generous. The task grew heavier and the skies darker. Lincoln simply worked harder, and he learned to pray. From somewhere came the strength to meet each crisis as it arose. Finally, the assassin's bullet brought him rest. He now lives forever enshrined in the hearts of his countrymen.

Lincoln dared to undertake a heavy task. He had the energy and honesty to see it through, and the wisdom to turn to the Giver of all perfect gifts in his hour of need. This simple formula has never yet failed and it will not fail for you.

Henry Eyring receiving the Peter Debye Award from H. Dayton Walde of Humble Oil in Denver American Chemical Society meeting, January, 1964.

How do we grow? I am a physical chemist interested in how atoms and molecules behave. Many things about atoms and molecules are still not understood. Great numbers of experiments have been done which are but dimly understood by even their perpetrators. If you want to understand these experiments, the job is strictly up to you. There is no one to explain them to you.

How do you find things out? One procedure is to keep studying and learning until you are fully prepared with all known knowledge before trying to understand that which is new. If you do this, you will wait forever. The correct procedure is quite different. If you want to find something out start on it right now! Ulysses S. Grant said it something like this:

> The way to pay off the national debt is to pay off the national debt.

Let's apply this principle to Church teaching, for example. If you want to be a good teacher, start being a good teacher. Now! How? Learn what you can reasonably learn about the subject in hand and you'll discover you've learned a great deal about many other things. Also you'll find that you'll need this same information over and over again.

I have sometimes been lazy about going to the bottom of some mathematical proposition needed in my research and have spent considerable time figuring out ways of getting along without the information. The inevitable outcome of such a course is that the particular miserable question keeps recurring and recurring until you finally dive in and clean the matter up once and for all. You then wake up surprised to discover yourself on a peak with vast vistas in all directions, and you wonder why you didn't pay the honest price in the first place.

In teaching the Gospel, to be a good example is more important than to give a brilliant exposition of principles. Brother Lowell Bennion, from his wide experience in teaching in the L.D.S. Institute, points out that, when students are properly adjusted socially, their philosophical difficulties evapcrate like water. If you have the kindly human touch with faith in the Gospel, your students will feel it even though you murder the English language. If you don't have these prime requisites of integrity, you won't matter much as a teacher.

There is probably no better way to deepen faith in the Gospel than to try to think out how this magnificently complicated world came about. Only a profound scholar of the physical sciences is able to calculate the utter improbability of any universe arising by chance. There is a deep meaning running through all that touches our lives. The Gospel is to be found not only in the scriptures but in every detail of the world if we can but read it.

Developing in Others
a Determination
to Live the Gospel

THE SAVIOR, AFTER HIS RESURRECTION, MADE CLEAR TO
His disciples their responsibility to carry the Gospel
to every creature. In the last chapter of the Gospel
according to Mark, the Savior's injunction is recorded in
this way:

> Afterward he appeared unto the eleven as they sat
> at meat, and upbraided them with their unbelief and
> hardness of heart, because they believed not them which
> had seen him after he was risen.
> And he said unto them, Go ye into all the world,
> and preach the gospel to every creature.
> He that believeth and is baptized shall be saved;
> but he that believeth not shall be damned.
> And these signs shall follow them that believe; In
> my name shall they cast out devils; they shall speak with
> new tongues;
> They shall take up serpents; and if they drink any
> deadly thing, it shall not hurt them; they shall lay hands
> on the sick, and they shall recover. (Mark 16:14-18.)

The Lord, speaking through the Prophet Joseph
Smith, has made it equally clear that it is our responsi-
bility to develop in others a determination to live the
Gospel. In the Doctrine and Covenants we read:

> And the voice of warning shall be unto all people,

by the mouth of my disciples, whom I have chosen in
these last days.
    And they shall go forth and none shall stay them,
for I the Lord have commanded them. (Doctrine and
Covenants 1:4-5.)

Our responsibility is clear. How can we discharge it?
Elder Spencer W. Kimball, at a conference of Bonne-
ville Stake, told of a youthful experience which has
impressed him through the years. A speaker in a meeting
long ago said that, of course, the first generation remained
true to the faith because some of them had to die for the
Gospel, and the second generation was likewise faithful
because of the rigors of pioneering and the testimonies of
their parents; but the test will come with an easy-living,
forgetful third and fourth generation. Here the seeds of
apostasy may bear bitter fruit. Right then Brother Kimball resolved that at least one grandson of Heber C.
Kimball would not forget. A teacher had sent a well-
directed shaft to its mark, and had awakened a valiant
defender of the faith.

    Too often we forget that children are not born with
a knowledge of the Gospel. They must learn it line upon
line and precept upon precept. As Church workers we
must know the Gospel ourselves and teach it. Otherwise,
we will surely answer for our negligence before the
Eternal Judge.

    Sometimes we hear of the transgressions of the sons
or daughters of loyal members of the Church with the
explanation that the father was too busy saving others
to take care of his own. This is tragic when it happens,
but how often do we witness another kind of tragedy.
The careless father and mother very often raise children
who don't even know the rudiments of the Gospel. Only
a miracle—or some influence like the Sunday School—
can save them from the long, painful blundering process
of feeling their way from darkness into the light which
wise parents would have started them out with.

As you go back through the years, do you remember the kindly, smiling Sunday School teacher who made you proud to be his friend? He was a substantial member of the community—remember? On Sundays he came smiling and neatly-dressed, and welcomed you as a friend. His lessons sparkled with examples that you understood. Underneath it all you knew he believed the Gospel. He made a lasting impression on you.

I recall an occasion in which adult members of the Aaronic Priesthood gave the talks in sacrament meeting. The talks were excellent. Shortly afterward, six of the men were ordained elders. An excellent teaching job had been done here. How? Kindness did it, they said —a friendly smile—a word of encouragement, and they began doing what their mind had long told them they should do. We can't learn too early or too well the lesson to hate sin but to love the sinner.

Lowell Bennion, speaking from his wide experience in teaching in the LDS Institute at the University of Utah, said it this way: "At first I thought the big problem of university students would be questions in logic and philosophy, but I soon found out that when they were happy and socially accepted, their imagined difficulties melted away." The greatest of all teachers:

> . . . called the Twelve and saith unto them, If any man desire to be first, the same shall be last of all, and servant of all.
>
> And he took a child, and set him in the midst of them: and when he had taken him in his arms, he said unto them,
>
> Whosoever shall receive one of such children in my name receiveth me, and whosoever shall receive me receiveth not me, but him that sent me.

And a little later,

> And whosoever shall offend one of these little ones that believe in me, it is better for him that a millstone

were hanged about his neck, and he were cast into the sea. (Mark 9:35-37, 42.)

In love and humility the Savior touched men's heart. May the Lord help us in our humble way to do the same.

Be Tolerant of Others

NO VIRTUE IS MORE BECOMING THAN HUMILITY, AND IN no way does humility shine more brightly than in the honest recognition of one's own limitations. Who has not been delighted by the down-to-earth speaker who knows when to say, "I don't know"?

Ringing down through the ages comes the voice of Gamaliel, a doctor of the law, member of the Sanhedrin and a teacher of Paul. We are told in Acts that Peter and the other apostles with him preached to the people in the temple. Then the high priest and the captain of the temple and the chief priests were worried about where they might lead. They arrested the brethren and took them before the council and accused them, saying:

> . . . Did not we straitly command you that ye should not teach in this name? and, behold, ye have filled Jerusalem with your doctrine, and intend to bring this man's blood upon us.
>
> Then Peter and the other apostles answered and said, We ought to obey God rather than men.
>
> The God of our fathers raised up Jesus, whom ye slew and hanged on a tree.
>
> Him hath God exalted with his right hand to be a Prince and a Savior, for to give repentance to Israel, and forgiveness of sins.
>
> And we are his witnesses of these things; and so is also the Holy Ghost, whom God hath given to them that obey him.

When they heard that, they were cut to the heart, and took counsel to slay them.

Then stood there up one in the council, a Pharisee, named Gamaliel, a doctor of the law, had in reputation among all the people, and . . . said unto them, Ye men of Israel, take heed to yourselves what ye intend to do as touching these men. . . .

And now I say unto you, Refrain from these men, and let them alone: for if this counsel or this work be of men, it will come to nought:

But if it be of God, ye cannot overthrow it; lest haply ye be found even to fight against God.

And to him they agreed: and when they had called the apostles, and beaten them, they commanded that they should not speak in the name of Jesus, and let them go.

And they departed from the presence of the council, rejoicing that they were counted worthy to suffer shame for his name.

And daily in the temple, and in every house, they ceased not to teach and preach Jesus Christ. (Acts 5:28-42.)

Latter-day Saints hold in grateful remembrance the names of other men who in modern times shielded the oppressed Saints from the vengeful destruction of the oppressor. High on this list stands the name of General Alexander W. Doniphan. General Doniphan was three years younger than the Prophet Joseph Smith and faithfully served as his legal counsel in Clay County, Missouri. During the Missouri persecutions, General Doniphan commanded militia under General Lucas, a bitter enemy of the Saints. The latter, by a ruse, had taken the Prophet and others of the brethren prisoners, convened a court martial, and sentenced them to death.

About midnight of Nov. 2, 1838, General Lucas wrote:

Brigadier General Doniphan—Sir: You will take Joseph Smith and the other prisoners into the public square of Far West, and shoot them at 9 o'clock tomorrow

morning. (Signed) Samuel D. Lucas, Major General
Commanding.

General Doniphan replied:

> It is cold-blooded murder. I will not obey your
> order. My brigade shall march for Liberty tomorrow
> morning at 8 o'clock; and if you execute these men, I will
> hold you responsible before an earthly tribunal, so help
> me God. (Signed) A.W. Doniphan, Brigadier General.[1]

Alexander Doniphan, who was only thirty years old
when this happened, always remained friendly to the
Saints, became a hero in the Mexican War, and served
two terms in the United States Senate. In May, 1874,
General Doniphan visited Utah and spent some time
with President Young. The man who had saved the life
of the Prophet was naturally a welcome guest in Salt
Lake City. The utter destruction of Jackson County,
foretold by the Prophet Joseph, had made a deep impression on the general. Doniphan was a tolerant, courage-
ous, good man who believed in justice, even when following his conscience might have ruined him.

Perhaps the greatest friend of our people was Colonel
Thomas L. Kane. A confidant of presidents of the United
States, he espoused our cause through all the years when
we were least popular, with no possibility of worldly
advantage. He and his father helped with the arrange-
ments for the Mormon Battalion.

Later, when Johnston's army was ready to invade
Utah, he negotiated with the President and with President
Brigham Young, thus shielding us from disaster. In fact,
he stood ready to help whenever the need arose. Apparently he had some reservations about our doctrines, since
he never joined the Church; but whatever these reservations were, tolerance and common humanity made him
our ever-faithful friend.

---

[1] Joseph Smith, *History of The Church of Jesus Christ of Latter-day Saints* Volume
III; Deseret News, Salt Lake City, Utah, 1905; pages 190, 191.

Army Advisory Conference on Explosives, Russell E. Duff, Henry Eyring, Paul M. Gross, Peter Debye, Ralph E. Gibson, Durham, N.C., 1964.

Will Rogers said, "I never met a man I didn't like." People are generally tolerant of those whom they take the trouble to understand.

Tolerance breeds tolerance in return. The great colonizer, President Brigham Young, welcomed Thomas B. Marsh and Orson Hyde back after the grave mistakes they had made in Missouri.

Big men are tolerant without compromising their principles.

PART VI

Truth for the Young

If I Were You—Advice to Young Men

E ACH GENERATION MUST MEET ITS OWN SPECIAL PROB-
lems. Since I was seventeen as World War I ended,
I missed the war itself but observed its effects on friends
and neighbors. Many veterans returned from the war
old beyond their years, matured by stress and suffering.
Promises to live better, made in the heat of battle, were
often kept. In 1918, as the war drew to its close, the
great influenza epidemic swept over the world, striking
down the weak and the strong alike. This was the pre-
lude to the booming twenties.

Actually life went on much as it had done before
and as it goes on now. The old advised the young and
were politely ignored, just as now. I remember in 1919
an assembly at the University of Arizona in which members of the Class of 1902 proffered their advice to the
students. As a budding mining engineer it seemed to me
that some genuine fossils would have been much more
instructive and interesting. After all, how could these
oldsters understand the changing problems of students
twenty years their junior? Having learned nothing, I
now tender my advice to you.

One never really grows old as long as there are
higher peaks still to be climbed. If each day brings a new
challenge with an opportunity to pit one's best efforts
against a hostile environment life remains as interesting
and stirring at sixty as at twenty. "Ah, but a man's
reach should exceed his grasp, Or what's a heaven for?"

Plan big and accept defeat only as another step along the road to success. Fortunate is the man or woman who finds such a challenge in his daily work.

Youth is the time to chart one's course so that one's path will always lead toward higher ground. Goals that are to remain challenging as one's powers wane must extend beyond mortality and beyond self.

> Thou shalt love the Lord thy God with all thy heart, and with all thy soul, and with all thy mind.
> This is the first and great commandment.
> And the second is like unto it, Thou shalt love thy neighbor as thyself. (Matt. 22:37-39.)

The assurance of a life to come gives a meaning to mortality that it cannot possibly possess without this assurance.

If I were you, I would resolve to live in such a way that I had nothing to hide. There is no surer way to have nothing to regret.

The earlier one can find a workable answer to Pontius Pilate's question "What is truth?" (John 18:38), the earlier one can get out of the shoals of life and set out on the main voyage.

A very few sentences suffice to outline the simple philosophy that guides me. This magnificent universe operates according to an over-all plan. The Planner is so great He can be, and is, interested even in me. Because of His interest, man is here according to a plan which is in accord with the divine purpose. Since it is obvious that individuals are born under unequal circumstances and ordinarily seem to fail to receive justice in this life, it is natural for me to believe in an immortality which achieves this justice. Since an all-wise God can communicate with man to man's advantage, such communication is to be expected. The Church of Jesus Christ as restored through the Prophet *is* this communicated plan which leads to eternal progress. Believing in this over-all destiny, I can still achieve it only by an infinitude of decisions made one at a time.

If I were you, I would get this master plan in mind, believing that if all the little things are done well, one by one, the big things will take care of themselves.

Now is Forever

Ricky Nelson, son of Ozzie and Harriet Nelson, while on location in Arizona for the filming of "Rio Bravo," expressed the teenager's concern over adult criticism.

The *Deseret News and Salt Lake Telegram* quotes him this way:

> As far as I have been able to find out, older people have been complaining about the wildness of kids for centuries. My father insists his generation was exposed to the same type of criticism that we are today. I just don't understand why the accused so often have turned into the accusers.

Ricky, just by growing older your father's generation has learned some things that they did not understand at your age and that you do not understand now. You will never quite understand your father until you stand in his place. Because he is so anxious that you avoid his mistakes, he must try to help you. Be patient with him as you expect him to be patient with you.

On one occasion, like Daniel of old, I was thrown to the lions. I was sent to teach a Sunday School class of twenty fine, upstanding 12-year-olds. To their credit they knew the Articles of Faith backwards and forwards and were fair on Church history and excellent on the Bible stories they had been studying.

On the other hand, most of them were completely uninhibited with regard to talking and expressing themselves generally; and any manners they may have been taught were, for the time being, forgotten. When I talked fast enough on subjects that interested them, I could be heard above the uproar. Finally, since love and kindness were clearly wasted on them, only stern measures remained to be tried.

In a voice that betrayed my agitation I told them to keep still. This surprised and quieted them, and I was able to proceed. With firmness and fast talking and with frequent questions, we then had a fairly pleasant time the rest of the hour.

Concerned as to what they would tell their parents, I explained to several fathers what had happened. All said they had heard nothing of it from their children. Apparently this experience which was unnerving to me was not even worthy of comment by the children.

Having taught graduate students in college for 30 years, I was surprised how much I did not know about 12-year-olds. However, my mind was filled with compassion for all the untrained teachers who are in rooms each Sunday morning with twenty to thirty ungoverned dynamos. Lots of class participation seemed to solve the problem. The students liked to tell the lesson stories themselves and to answer questions. It was surprising to me to see that they listened fairly well to each other.

I have always loved our bishops for their long hours of selfless service. I now add to those I honor and love the dedicated teachers of 12-year-olds.

Actually I would welcome returning to the fray, since I am sure the key to success lies in giving the students the initiative in some closely regulated fashion. It is heartening to have seen a lot of other 12-year-olds grow into fine men and women. Although 12-year-olds are not ready for a philosophical exposition of Gospel principles, they will be ready for this when they are 16. My experiences with this class have led me to formulate such a statement which I hope may appeal to the students who are just a little bit older.

The Gospel answers for me the why about the world
and about my existence, much as science answers the
how. Life loses most of its meaning unless we have a
satisfactory answer as to where we came from and where
we are going. We believe that as intelligences we have
always existed. In a pre-existent state we became the
spirit children of our Father in heaven. When the council
in heaven was held, we elected to accept earth life as a
period of growth and development and probation. We
were born into the world having our free agency; i.e.,
with the right to choose to do either good or evil.

Death is not the end but only brings a transfer of
our activities, and in due course our spirits will be clothed
with a resurrected body. Our position in the hereafter
will depend upon our conduct here, and we can continue
to grow more perfect in goodness, wisdom and knowledge
throughout the eternities.

Earth life has its great significance as the bridge
between these two eternities. In undertaking any journey,
the destination we reach depends on the road we take,
how well we make our plans and how vigorously we
carry through.

The Gospel is the Lord's plan for the journey. Because we have our free agency, we can accept or reject it.
Finally, even if we accept the Gospel plan, we can carry
through in a way that will get us into the celestial kingdom or we can reap an eternity of vain regrets for what
might have been.

In this age of space travel, we are reminded every
day of the painstaking care that goes into the launching
of a satellite which is to journey out into the unknown.
When a man is placed on the satellite, this meticulous
care will be increased by an order of magnitude. The
"count down" now is a check, item by item, to be certain
that every device is operating according to plan. The
failure of a single part to operate properly can mean
failure of the whole enterprise. In our fastest planes the

motto might well read: "In a jet you make but one mistake."

Is it strange then, that in the journey of life we are expected to comply with certain ordinances and live in accord with Gospel principles? If we do not do this, we will always regret it. Some choices we make right now are forever!

"... Young Men Shall See Visions"

NEVER IN HISTORY HAS THE WORLD CHANGED SO FAST. Jules Verne's wonderful tale, "Around the World in 80 Days," seems almost quaint in a world where man-made satellites circle the earth in 90 minutes at 18,000 miles an hour. These devices click back to us their multiple radio messages about temperature and radiation and other secrets that could only be guessed at a few years ago.

As man ventures out into space, will his ship be destroyed by being pelted with meteors and meteoric dust? Will he be injured by cosmic rays and ultra-violet light? How hot will his ship get in the glaring sun with no air to carry away the heat? These questions and dozens more are being answered by our manned satellites as we sit and listen while they orbit about the earth.

Indeed, any sensible scientific question which man is able to formulate as an experiment brings back its answer "yes" or "no." Thus we penetrate ever deeper into mysteries that yesterday were unanswerable.

Striking the moon with a missile across the intervening 241,000 miles is already an accomplished fact. A trip to the moon—and, eventually, beyond—is now taken for granted.

Such a journey offers many problems, which will be solved by some adventurous young men who see visions.

What is the effect of this breathtaking speed in scientific matters on man's religious outlook? Our century has witnessed a turning away from the mechanistic determinism of the 19th Century which led the famous scientist, La Place, to answer Napoleon's query about God with, "Sire, I have no need of that hypothesis." Many men these days, scientists among the rest, feel they have very great need for turning to the Supreme Architect of the universe. The uncertainty principle of quantum mechanics is a humbler approach to the mysteries of creation than mechanistic determinism.

In the autumn of 1957, in Houston, Texas the Welch Foundation invited the top nuclear physicists and chemists from all over the world to a symposium. At a dinner, twelve of the most distinguished were seated at a table. As one of the scientific advisers to the Welch Foundation I was privileged to be there. Mr. Malone, a trustee of the foundation, said, "Dr. Eyring, how many of these gentlemen believe in a Supreme Being?" I answered, "I don't know but I'll ask."

So twelve people were asked and every one said, "I believe." All of these students of the exact sciences —two of them Nobel Prize winners—saw in the universal order about them evidence for a Supreme Being.

Men like Harvey Fletcher, Carl J. Christensen and A. Ray Olpin as young men saw visions of a better scientific world and their dreams have come true in improvements in the telephone. Tracy Hall, with his associates, has succeeded in the age-old dream of synthesizing diamonds. Such examples could be multiplied almost endlessly.

It is gratifying that the youth of the Church are learning both about the universe and about the Gospel. Yet it is more gratifying that they are adding to their unparalleled vision of material things that deeper and more satisfying vision of life everlasting.

PART VII

Great Scientists and Truth

Sir Isaac Newton

A S ONE WATCHES ECHO I CROSS THE SKY, ONE CAN'T help wondering what Sir Isaac Newton would say about this man-made moon, for it is through the application of his laws of mechanics that such a "miracle" is becoming increasingly commonplace. Almost three hundred years ago he wrote down the equation which explains how a falling moon can fall forever toward the earth without hitting it, providing the moon is above the atmosphere (thus avoiding forces which would cause it to burn up) and is moving horizontally at around 18,000 miles an hour.

Though only a careful and penetrating study of science would make it possible for one to more fully understand Newton's scientific contributions, still all of us can gain much of benefit by becoming better acquainted with his scientific discoveries, his accomplishments and his life.

Good scientific endeavor, like good carpentry, professional golf or any other skill, is in large measure the product of at least two factors: a great amount of hard work and a degree of natural ability. Sir Isaac Newton was a master craftsman in science. By trying to understand and become acquainted with his life and accomplishments we should be able to better understand and appreciate the exciting world in which we live.

Sir Isaac Newton was born Christmas day, 1642, in Stuart, England, seven years before Charles the First was overthrown by Cromwell. He was born into a world of political foment like our modern world, and his work started a scientific revolution which challenged men's minds as modern science challenges us today. His father, Isaac, was an independent farmer but was regarded by his neighbors as "a wild, extravagant, weak man." His mother, Hannah Ayscough, was thrifty, industrious and a good manager. Young Isaac was born prematurely just after his father's death and was reared by his grandparents. His mother's three children by her second marriage were not notably gifted. Newton inherited an income of eighty pounds sterling per year from his father's and mother's estate. This was enough so that he was never in financial need.

Even as a boy Newton was not robust. Instead of playing rough games, he spent his time inventing interesting mechanical toys such as water wheels, a toy mill to grind flour which was turned by a captive mouse. He also flew lighted lanterns from kites at night to give the superstitious something to talk about. Newton never married. While going to preparatory school in Woolsthorpe before going to Cambridge, he fell in love with and became engaged to Miss Storey. He was then nineteen, and although they drifted apart and she later married a Mr. Vincent, he always cherished a warm affection for his one and only sweetheart.

Newton's equation for a circular orbit sets the centripetal force equal to the gravitational attraction and thus obtains the relation:

$$r^3 = t^2 \times 31.8 \text{ billion}$$

Here r is the distance in miles between the center of the earth and the center of the satellite while t is the time in hours required to go around the earth. If a satellite is orbiting a thousand miles above the earth this gives r = 5,000 (since the radius of the earth is 4,000 miles) and we calculate for the time of going around the earth the value t = 1.97 hours or 1 hour and 58 minutes. Satellites nearer to the earth go around it in correspondingly less time. Further, since it takes about twenty-eight days for the moon to go around the earth, it follows from the above equation that the moon is about 240,000 miles from the earth's center.

If one swings a bucket of water over one's head, the water remains in the bucket even when the bucket is upside down, providing it is swinging fast enough. The whirling bucket of water exerts a distinct pull on the arm. This pull is called the centripetal force and it is proportional to the square of the velocity of the bucket of water multiplied by the weight of bucket plus water, divided by the radius of the circle in which the bucket is travelling (the length of one's arm in this example). Newton recognized that the moon whirling in its orbit must exert just such a centripetal pull and that it must be held in its course by earth's gravitational attraction which pulls it toward the earth just as it pulls any other falling body. Now it is easy to perform a quantitative experiment to check this explanation of the moon's motion.

First, we drive a nail into the center of a polished table top. Next, we attach to a polished steel ball, which is lying on the table, one end of a wire which in turn is tied by its other end to a weighing scale. The other end of the weighing scale is then wired to the nail. This arrangement is illustrated in Figure 1. Now the ball, which has a weight, W, measured in pounds, is made to rotate on the table top with a velocity, v, measured in feet per second. This velocity is equal to the circumference of the circle, $2\pi r$, described by the ball (measured in feet) divided by the time, t (in seconds) required for the ball to make one revolution. The pull, P, in pounds, which one can read on the scale, is then the centripetal force and has the value

$$P = \frac{W}{32r} \left(\frac{2\pi r}{t}\right)^2$$

Now Newton surmised that in the case of the moon, the moon's weight was the attractive force which balanced

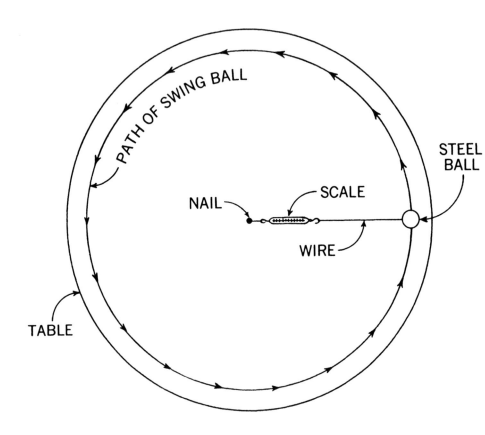

Fig. 1 An experiment which measures the centripetal force which goes into one side of Newton's equation for the forces holding a satellite in its orbit.

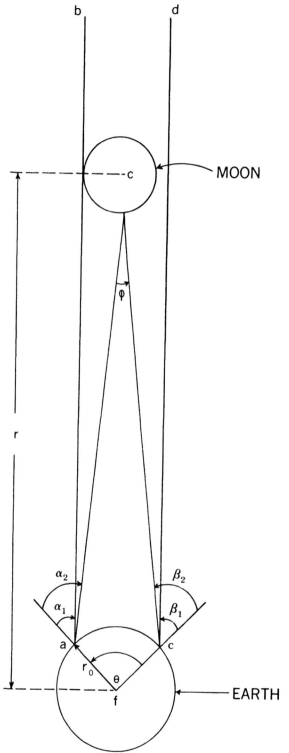

Fig 2 Triangulations necessary to measure the radius of the earth, r_0, and the radius of the moon orbit, r.

the centripetal force, P. More than that, knowing Kepler's law as given in equation 1 he knew that the weight of the moon must fall off with the square of the distance of the moon's center from the center of the earth. Thus if W signifies the weight the moon has at the earth's surface, at the distance, r_0, from the earth's center, its weight in its orbit will be

$$P = W \left(\frac{r_0}{r}\right)^2$$

Finally, Newton equated the two values for the pull, P, in equations 2 and 3 and obtained the result

$$W \left(\frac{r_0}{r}\right)^2 = \frac{W}{32r} \left(\frac{2\pi r}{t}\right)^2$$

in which he knew that the period, t, of the moon's rotation was 28 days. By triangulation he could determine the radius of the earth, r_0, and the distance between the moon's and the earth's centers, r. The weight, W, of the moon at the earth's surface cancels out of equation 4 so that it does not have to be determined.

Measuring the earth's radius, r_0, and the moon's orbit, r, is easy to understand by reference to Figure 2. A distance ae on the earth's surface is measured by the best surveying techniques. Then at the point a on the earth's surface, the angle α_1 which a distant star makes with the vertical is measured at the same instant that one measures the value β_1 for the same angle at point c. Because the star is far away, the two lines ab and ed are parallel, so that $\alpha_1 + \beta_1 = \theta$ the angle of arc corresponding to the measured length, ac, along the earth's circumference. This enables us to calculate the earth's radius r_0. If now in the same way at the two points a and c on the earth's surface we simultaneously sight at the same spot on the moon and measure the angles α_2 and β_2, one can verify that $\Phi = (\alpha_2 + \beta_2) - (\alpha_1 + \beta_1)$. now knowing the angles θ and Φ and the length ac we can scale with a ruler or calculate the distance to the moon's surface. Next, measuring the angle between opposite sides of the moon from a point on the earth, we get the moon's diameter. Finally, we can calculate the distance r between centers.

When Newton first substituted the accepted values for t, r_0 and r into equation 4 the two sides of the equation failed to agree. This meant that either his theory was wrong or there was a mistake in the accepted values. Newton, great scientist that he was, didn't publish his results, but just waited. In a half dozen years the earth's radius was redetermined and with the new values equation 4 was confirmed. In order to usher in this magnificent scientific triumph, the 22-year-old Newton had to invent the calculus, formulate the law of gravitational attraction and put Galilean mechanics into quantitative form. It is hoped that this simplified but quantitative description of this enormously important scientific victory gives some insight into the methods of science.

Perhaps those who find this simplified treatment of the motion of heavenly bodies difficult to comprehend will understand better why the scriptures are not written as scientific textbooks. Things which must be trivially simple to the Lord are often inscrutable mysteries to us. These results provide an interesting perspective on eternal progression. There is apparently no end to learning and no end of things to learn.

To tell Newton's story without discussing some of the great men who preceded and succeeded him is to distort history. Even though we can do little more than quote names and dates, this should at least help to give a more balanced perspective. Copernicus, who was born February 19, 1473, was just nineteen years old when Columbus astounded the world by discovering America. It is no wonder that Copernicus was moved to study the planets and to reject Ptolemy's picture of epicycles. In its place, he developed our modern picture of the earth going around the sun. This so offended the religious sensibilities of the churchmen of that day that Galileo Galilei, born December 14, 1564, who subscribed to the Copernican view, escaped being burned by the Inquisition only by recanting. Giordano Bruno, born in 1550, was not so fortunate. He was burned at the stake by the Inquisition for his assertions that the earth went around the sun instead of the sun going around the earth. Leibnitz, born in Germany on June 21, 1646, has been called "the most universal scientific genius of modern times." He was co-discoverer with Newton of the calculus and was famous for his studies in philosophy. Like Newton, Leibnitz was a religious man.

Newton is reputed to have said, "If I have seen a little farther than others, it is because I have stood on the shoulders of giants." We have briefly mentioned several in the preceding paragraph. Three of these "giants" who directly influenced Newton's scientific endeavor were 1. the Frenchman Descartes, from whom Newton learned analytical geometry; 2. Kepler, the German, whose fundamental laws of planetary motion formed the basis for Newton's enunciation of the Universal Law of Gravitation; and 3. the Italian Galileo from whom he learned two of the three laws of his mechanics. It was, of course, necessary to have this exciting building material, but it took the genius of Newton to develop it into Newtonian mechanics.

It might be interesting to recall Kepler's laws of planetary motion:

1. The planets move around the sun in ellipses; the sun is at one focus of these ellipses.
2. The line joining the sun and a planet sweeps out equal areas in equal times.
3. The square of the time for one complete revolution of each planet is proportional to the cube of its average distance from the sun.

These laws are just as true for man-made satellites as for any other heavenly bodies. Our equation 1 is simply

Kepler's third law and we have already seen that it applies equally well to Echo I and to the moon. The interested student should borrow from the library and read the English translation of Newton's *Principia.*

It is quite natural to ask what this great man thought about God. Was he religious or was he just too busy to be interested in such questions? E.T. Bell on page 95 of his interesting book *Men of Mathematics* has this to say:

> As for theology, Newton was an unquestioning believer in an all-wise Creator of the universe and in his own inability—like that of the boy on the seashore—to fathom the entire ocean of truth in all its depths. He therefore believed that there were not only many things in heaven beyond his philosophy, but plenty on earth as well, and he made it his business to understand for himself what the majority of intelligent men of his time accepted without dispute (to them it was as natural as common sense)—the traditional account of creation. . . . He . . . therefore put what he considered his really serious efforts on attempts to prove that the prophecies of Daniel and the poetry of the apocalypse made sense, and on chronological researches whose object was to harmonize the dates of the Old Testament with those of history.

Newton's book *The Chronology of Ancient Kingdoms* will interest many people. He was busy working on it for the last thirty years of his life and was not quite through revising it when he died at eighty-five. This indicates his deep concern with religious questions.

As long as civilization lasts, teachers will tell students about the incomparable Sir Isaac Newton. Thanks to his theories we predict the behavior of satellites with the same split-second accuracy with which eclipses have been predicted since his time. It would take many volumes to sketch the fruits of his contributions of calculus to mathematics and of mechanics to physics and astronomy. He also showed how white light could be split into all the colors of the rainbow by using a glass prism and explained what all his discoveries meant.

One naturally might ask: What can I adapt from Newton's life that will help *me?* Everyone can work as hard as Newton and everyone can be as honest. Newton was searching for the truth wherever it led him. This you and I should do, working always with Newton's dedication and faith.

Max Planck

E LSEWHERE IN THIS BOOK WE MENTIONED NEWTON AND his laws of mechanics which have been used to predict successfully the motions of the earth and of the planets and more recently of the satellites shot into space by man. In fact these laws were so generally successful that the great German philosopher Immanuel Kant and the French mathematician La Place developed separately the nebular hypothesis, based on Newton's laws, to explain the origin of our solar system. In this theory as in the description of the universe given in our scriptures the gravitational law causes the stars and planets to revolve around larger centers of mass. The giant star cluster or galaxy to which our solar system belongs is like a great grinding stone 75,000 light years in diameter and our solar system is about 30,000 light years from its center. This giant "wheel" rotates on its axis once every 200 million years. In turn we are surrounded by numerous other similar galaxies as far out into space as we can see with the best telescopes. The 200-inch telescope on Mt. Palomar, in southern California, enables us to see a distance of two billion light years. A light year is the distance light travels in a year going at a speed of 186,000 miles per second.

La Place went on to show that if Newton's laws held for the atoms and if at a certain instant we know the position and velocity of each atom then it is possible to calculate the behavior of every atom at any time in the future or in the past. Since man is made of atoms it looked to La Place as if his every thought and action were predestined by immutable mechanical laws. This was Calvinist predestination with a vengeance! However, it was proved in 1900 by Max Planck in Germany that very small particles like atoms and electrons do not obey Newtonian mechanics. Instead they obey a new wave mechanics which grew out of the quantum theory discovered by Planck. According to the new mechanics it is impossible to know the position and velocity of a particle exactly at the same time. This makes Newton's laws inapplicable and this argument for strict predestination disappears. In place of predestination the new mechanics enables us to predict future events with very high probability but not with certainty.

Before looking into his scientific contributions it might be interesting to learn a little about Planck's personal life. I remember very well first seeing him at physics colloquia in Berlin in the fall of 1929. He was tall, earnest, reserved and polite; the typical college professor in appearance. He was then seventy-one years old, having been born in Kiel, Germany, April 23, 1858. Planck came from a distinguished family of lawyers, public servants and scholars. His father, Julius Wilhelm von Planck, was professor of constitutional law at Kiel University and later at Göttingen. Planck was careful and exact in his thinking and like Millikan worked while standing at a tall desk.

Planck enjoyed excellent health and climbed a 12,000-foot mountain peak after he was sixty years old. His good health continued until his death in his 89th year. He received many honors. Besides his receiving the Nobel prize, the name of the famous Kaiser Wilhelm Institute was changed to the Max Planck Institute and a small planet was named after him. He was conservative in his general outlook but a cautious revolutionary in science. He wrote scientific papers with Clausius, Helmholtz and Kirchhoff—all scientists of the first rank. Among his students were two Nobel prize winners, Bothe and von Laue. Another student was Lise Meitner who with Niels Bohr brought the news during wartime of the splitting of the atom in Germany. This precipitated the feverish research that became the Manhattan Project and resulted in atomic and later hydrogen bombs.

In spite of his great successes and many honors his life was in many ways tragic. His first marriage lasted from 1887 until his wife's death in 1909. Of their four children the first two were twin girls who each died bearing her first child. His oldest son Karl was killed at Verdun in 1916 during World War I and the other son Erwin was killed by the Nazis in January 1945 for having been involved in the plot against Hitler. His daughters' children were educated in his home. From his second marriage he had one son born in 1911. Prior to and during World War II he did what he could to prevent cruelty to the Jews and tried especially to intervene in behalf of Fritz Haber, a famous chemist in whose laboratory I worked in 1929-1930. His love of country made him feel deeply depressed at the destruction in both World Wars I and II. In the latter war he lost everything including his home and an invaluable library. After recovering from double pneumonia at the age of 88 he died a year later in Göttingen on October 4, 1947.

One can't help wondering what constituted Planck's genius. His scientific performance is startling enough. For 250 years the laws of Newton had passed every test successfully, piling one triumph upon another. By 1900, however, a genuine failure of Newtonian mechanics was apparent. According to these laws the light, coming from a hot "black box," when spread out as a rainbow by sending it through a prism should be more intense the further you go toward the violet end of the rainbow. But this is not what happens. The quantitative explanation of this contradiction forced Planck to deduce that light was particle-like and was sent out in discreet pulses or quanta. Thus was born the mighty quantum theory which has resolved a thousand enigmas and made man incomparably more powerful in controlling the forces of nature. If one really gets a fundamental answer to some seemingly unimportant question it often provides the key to understanding otherwise obscure universal truths. Planck was thus concerned with calculating the amount of radiation in an enclosed space and how the amount of the radiant energy changes with the temperature, and particularly how it varies for the different colors of the rainbow. Anyone who has felt the warm sunlight on his face must marvel that this radiant energy has crossed the ninety million miles of empty space between the earth and the sun in the preceding seven and one half minutes. If sunlight is passed through a glass prism it can be separated into all the colors of the rainbow and the heating power for the different colors in the different parts of the spectrum is different. This heating power can be measured by putting a thermometer with a blackened bulb into the various parts of the spectrum and reading the temperature rise. When this is done carefully a profound divergence between experiment and classical theory arises.

Classical radiation theory predicts that the radiant energy from a hot source will increase progressively as one goes from red to violet, becoming infinitely high in the extreme violet. This is known as the ultraviolet catastrophe. In fact the catastrophe never materializes. Experimentally the intensity of radiant energy doesn't keep increasing from the red to the violet; it reaches a maximum for the intermediate colors. This anomaly is what Planck succeeded in explaining. The classical theory assumed that the bits of radiant energy could be emitted in lumps of all sizes. By careful mathematical analysis Planck found that it was possible to retain all the other features of the accepted theory of radiation and still explain the observed facts if he assumed that light must be emitted in lumps or quanta of a size proportional to their frequency (γ). Very reluctantly he made this revolutionary assumption. In this way the quantum theory was born. Light occurs only in lumps or quanta having the energy (hγ). Thus we think of light as having a distinct particle-like quality and yet in other ways it behaves very much like sound waves or water waves do in the way in which the wave motion passes through holes or bends around corners.

From this simple beginning it was found that it is necessary to revise Newtonian mechanics as it applies to very small particles such as molecules or atoms and adopt in its place the theory that has become known as the wave mechanics. Just as Planck's quantum theory, when applied to light, revealed the particle-like nature of light, so when it was applied to particles, it revealed the fact that particles sometimes act like waves. With this discovery of the wave nature of matter we were obliged to give up the strict Newtonian deterministic mechanical motion of atoms and molecules and adopt in its place the wave mechanics which can only predict that something is very likely to happen. This change had a revolutionary effect on the thinking of scientists. One consequence of this is greater humility. Much more of the workings of this divinely-organized universe have become clear as a result of Planck's findings that light is particle-like and always turns up in lumps or quanta of energy (hγ). Here h is Planck's universal constant.

Max Planck was a deeply religious person. The serious student of science and religion will want to read his entire "SCIENTIFIC AUTOBIOGRAPHY" (Philosophical Library, New York). We must content ourselves here with one brief quotation from pages 182 and 183.

> Having now learned to know the demands which religion, on one hand and science on the other hand, place on our attitude to the most sublime problems of a generalized world outlook, let us now examine whether and to what extent these different demands can be mutu-

ally reconciled. First of all, it is self evident that this examination may extend only to those laws in which religion and natural science conflict with each other. For there are wide spheres where they have absolutely nothing to do with each other. Thus all the problems of ethics are outside of the field of natural science, whereas the dimensions of the universal constants are without relevance for religion.

On the other hand, religion and natural science do have a point of contact in the issue concerning the existence and nature of a supreme power ruling the world, and here the answers given by them are to a certain degree at least comparable. As we have seen, they are by no means mutually contradictory, but are in agreement, first of all on the point that there exists a rational world order independent from man, and secondly, on the vein that the character of this world order can never be directly known but can only be indirectly recognized or suspected. Religion employs in this connection its own characteristic symbols, while natural science uses measurements founded on sense experiences. Thus nothing stands in our way— and our instinctive intellectual striving for a unified world picture demands it—from identifying with each other the two everywhere active and yet mysterious forces: The world order of natural science and the God of religion. Accordingly, the deity which the religious person seeks to bring closer to himself by his palpable symbols, is consubstantial with the power acting in accordance with natural laws for which the sense data of the scientist provide a certain degree of evidence.

Apparently the best minds, like the humblest, when confronted with the problems of the ultimate meaning of things, must and do walk by faith.

The Church has always championed truth whatever its source as emphasized in the thirteenth Article of Faith. The author is indebted to Professor Angus M. Woodbury for gathering together the following statements which outline the position of our Church in such matters:

"The glory of God is intelligence or in other words light and truth."

"Ye shall know the truth and the truth shall make you free." John 8:31-32.

"Seek ye diligently and teach one another words of wisdom; yea, seek ye out of the best books words of wisdom; seek learning even by study and also by faith." D&C 88.

"Man cannot be saved faster than he gains knowledge. It is impossible for a man to be saved in ignorance." D&C 131:6, 93:36.

"The principle of knowledge is the principle of salvation." Joseph, Smith, *History of the Church*, 5:387. (Research)

"One of the grand fundamental principles of 'Mormonism' is to receive truth (open mind) let it come from whence it may." *Ibid.*, 5:499.

"The most predominant point of difference between Latter-day Saints and sectarians is that the latter are all circumscribed by some peculiar creed, which deprives its members from believing anything not contained therein, whereas the LDS have *no creed*, but are ready to believe all true principles that exist, as they are made manifest from time to time. . . .

"We ought to gather together all the good and true principles which are in the world, and keep them; otherwise we shall never become pure Mormons." *Deseret News*, Jan. 21, 1857.

"Our religion will not clash with nor contradict the facts of science in any particular." Discourses of Brigham Young, pp. 397-398.

Brigham Young said on March 29, 1874 at St. George: "Educate yourselves and your children; learn not only the common branches but all pertaining to the arts and sciences." Bleak's Annals of Southern Utah Mission, p. 276.

Brigham Young said at Nephi, Utah: "Place good teachers in the school rooms and have beautiful gardens and teach them to know and enjoy the beauties of flowers and plants and their uses—when old enough, place within their reach the advantages and benefits of a scientific education. Let them study the formation of the earth, the organization of the human system and other sciences. Take for instance, the young ladies now before me, as well as the young men, and form a class in geology, in chemistry or mineralogy; and not confine their studies to theory only, but let them put in practice what they learn from books, by defining the nature of the soil, the composition or decomposition of a rock, how the earth was formed, its probable age, etc. All these are problems which science attempts to solve, although some of the views of our great scholars are undoubtedly very speculative. In the study of the sciences I have named, our young folks will learn how it is that, traveling in our mountains, we frequently see sea-shells, shells of the oyster, clam, etc. Ask our boys and girls to explain these things and they are not able to do so, but establish classes for the study of the sciences and they will become acquainted with the various facts they furnish in regard to the condition of the earth." *Deseret News,* April 18, 1874, p. 6.

March 29, 1874. Brother Brigham . . . remarked that he would like the people to study chemistry, astronomy and kindred sciences that we might know and comprehend what we used and had to do with every day and learn the component parts of the elements that surround us and be able to make them subservient to the building up of Zion. Journal of Charles L. Walker, p. 612.

Louis Pasteur

L OUIS PASTEUR WAS BORN IN DOLE, FRANCE, DECEMBER
27, 1822, the son of one of Napoleon's soldiers who
had won the Legion of Honor in military campaigns
serving the emperor. After his military service ended,
Joseph Pasteur, Louis' father, settled down in Solins,
France, and opened a little tannery. Louis' mother,
Jeanne Etiennette Roqui, was a gardener's daughter, a
near neighbor of Joseph. Joseph asked for her hand in
marriage, was accepted and they were extremely happy
in their humble little home. Pasteur was their only son,
but he had several sisters to whom he was always deeply
attached. Pasteur was educated at the Royal College of
Besancon and the Ecole Normale of Paris from which he
was graduated in 1847 at the age of 25. He taught then
in Dijon and later at Strassburg, Alsace. In Strassburg
he met and, on May 29, 1849, married Marie Laurent,
the lovely daughter of the new Rector of the Academy of
Strassburg. Marie was a loving companion and unselfish
supporter of Louis the rest of his life. In a little house
near one of the laboratories he had built, he died in the
late afternoon on September 28, 1895, of paralysis, ac-
companying repeated strokes. He was attended by his
wife and children.

It would be difficult to choose a person in all of
science who surpassed Pasteur in his contributions to
biology and medicine, as well as to chemistry. His first
research was in chemistry, in a field that still intrigues
chemists.

To understand Pasteur's work it will be helpful to

make some preliminary observations. Polaroid is made by taking a plastic made of long alcohol molecules, stretching the plastic in one direction to a still greater length, which causes all the molecules to line up parallel to each other. Iodine is then dissolved in the plastic, the iodine molecules lining up in their turn parallel to the long alcohol molecules. As a result, only that light penetrates a polaroid sheet which vibrates perpendicular to the length of the alcohol molecules. The other half of the light which vibrates parallel to the molecular axes is absorbed. If one looks at a source of light through a polaroid sheet, the light looks only half as bright as without the polaroid. If one places a second polaroid sheet in front of his eyes parallel to the first, he still can see half as much light as with no polaroid. If one now rotates one of the sheets through 90 degrees around an axis perpendicular to the light path, all the light is absorbed.

If the light traverses a tube filled with water placed in between the two polaroid sheets nothing is changed. However, if sugar is dissolved in the tube, the sheets of polaroid do not transmit as much light when the axes of the molecules in the two sheets lie parallel as when one sheet is rotated through an angle whose magnitude is proportional to the amount of dissolved sugar. There are, however, two kinds of sugar molecules. One requires that the near sheet of polaroid be rotated clockwise to produce maximum brightness, while for the other kind, the required rotation is counterclockwise. The first kind of molecules may be thought of as like the right hand and the rotation is said to be dextro-rotatory, while the second type of molecules are mirror images of the first, and may be compared to left hands, and are said to be levo-rotatory. The instrument used to measure whether molecules are levo- or dextro-rotatory is called a polarimeter. An astounding thing about life on this earth is that every form of life grows by incorporating only the right-handed sugars and the left-handed amino acids into their structure. If the other kinds of molecules are present in the food, they are rejcted. When a chemist makes sugars or amino acids, as he easily can, the left- and right-handed varieties occur in equal amounts.

Pasteur was the first to isolate the "unnatural" kind of molecules from a mixture of the two kinds by letting bacteria eat the natural kind. He also noticed that when molecular mixtures crystallize, the two kinds of molecules form slightly different crystal forms distinguishable by the appearance of characteristic tiny faces which can then be used to separate the two kinds of molecules. I think it is interesting to note that however the Lord arranged the detailed organization of living things, the result is a harmonious blending in which each living form feeds on lower forms having molecules with the appropriate type of symmetry.

After finishing this work, Pasteur worked night and day to find the cause and cure of the disease of silk worms which was destroying the silk industry in France. He found that by examining the moth under a microscope at the time it laid its eggs, he could tell whether the eggs would hatch into healthy silk worms. This method of selecting healthy eggs was adopted throughout Europe with tremendous success.

The same kind of infinite pains helped him understand fermentation and so save the French wine and beer industries. (One may well wonder whether saving the wine and beer industries was really a blessing!) As a matter of fact, Pasteur's process of pasteurizing, which consists in heating beers just hot enough to destroy unwanted ferments, was readily extended to the pasteurizing of milk and other fermentable substances. All these developments contributed to Pasteur's understanding of bacteria and how to deal with them and set the stage for the great advances he made in the control of the diseases which afflict mankind.

In Pasteur's day, doctors as well as the general populace believed in spontaneous generation. Diseases were supposed to "just happen" without any infection. In fact, Pasteur and others of his contemporaries such as Koch in Germany, were the first to isolate the bacteria through the use of the microscope and to prove that they were the infective agents that actually cause disease.

Our lack of understanding of cancer at present parallels the confused situation with respect to all diseases in Pasteur's time. If one could come out now with a sure cure for cancer, the excitement would approximate that caused by Pasteur's successful treatment of rabies in July, 1885. He and his assistants had done a tremendous number of experiments on hydrophobic, or rabid, dogs. In the process, they had found a way of making the virus less virulent. They extracted tissue from the brain of a rabid dog and let this tissue dry out in a suitable dry chamber for various lengths of time. Tissue that had been dried for fourteen days lost all power of infection even when mashed up in pure water and injected directly into the brain of a healthy dog. The tissue decreased in virulence progressively with the drying time from the extremely virulent fresh material to the non-virulent material which had been dried fourteen days.

Now Pasteur took a healthy dog and inoculated fourteen-day-old dried tissue into his brain. The next day, he inoculated thirteen-day-old material, and so on until on the fourteenth day the dog received tissue directly from the brain of a mad dog, which should have given him rabies in fourteen days. Nothing happened. Even when mad dogs were allowed to bite the treated animal he remained immune. Pasteur had finally solved the mystery of immunizing against rabies.

He still hesitated to try his method on human beings but on July 6, 1885, a little Alsatian boy, Joseph Meister, accompanied by his mother, came into his laboratory having been bitten from head to foot by a mad dog.

Joseph was sure to die if he was not treated. Other responsible people agreed with Pasteur that he was morally obligated to treat the lad. In spite of misgivings, he went ahead and treated Joseph by the exact procedure he had used successfully in immunizing dogs. The treatment was successful. Little Joseph Meister became the first person to be saved by inoculation after being bitten by a mad dog.

Pasteur was hailed by everyone, as he should have been, as the benefactor of all mankind. The honors bestowed on him on this occasion were greater than they had been when he had discovered the bacillus which cause the frightful disease of animals and human beings called anthrax. He had also shown how the disease could be controlled. The honors also surpassed even those he received when he saved France's silk industry. The Pasteur Institute was built in his honor in Paris by public subscription, and even though by this time Pasteur's health was failing, he devoted every effort to help others to carry on in the great tradition he had begun.

Pasteur had the simple faith that made him certain that he would live again with his family. These included his parents, his sisters, and the two little daughters who had preceded him in death, in addition to the devoted wife, married son and daughter and grandchildren whom he left behind.

We will quote only two of his many religious sayings:

> Science, which brings man nearer to God.
>
> There are two men in each one of us: the scientist, he who starts with a clear field and desires to rise to the knowledge of Nature through observation, experimentation and reasoning, and the man of sentiment, the man of belief, the man who mourns his dead children, and who cannot, alas, prove that he will see them again, but who believes that he will, and lives in the hope—the man who will not die like a vibrio, but who feels that the force that is within him cannot die.

Thus we glimpse a little of the life, the hopes and the faith of one of the greatest of all the life scientists.

There are many fine biographies of Pasteur. One of the best is *The Life of Pasteur*, translated from the French by Mrs. R.L. Devonshire in 1915. It was written by his son-in-law, Rene Vallery-Radot. Another is *Pasteur and His Work* by L. Descour.

Albert Einstein

ALBERT EINSTEIN WAS BORN IN ULM IN WURTENBURG, Germany, March 14, 1879. He went to the Luit-pold Gymnasium (high school) in Munich. He earned his Ph.D. in Switzerland and taught in Switzerland, in Prague and in Germany. Because of the Nazi persecutions in 1933 he left Berlin and became a professor at the Institute for Advanced Study in Princeton where he died April 18, 1957 at age 76. He married twice. In 1901 he married Mileva Marec, a fellow student from Serbia, by whom he had two sons, Hans Albert and Eduard. He and Mileva were divorced in 1916, and in 1917 he married his cousin, Elsa Einstein, who died in Princeton in 1936.

Everyone has seen pictures of him so I needn't describe him beyond saying that he was pleasant and straightforward in his dealings with other people. I first listened to Professor Einstein talk in Berlin in 1929 and 1930. He was even then world renowned. For about the last twelve years I spent at Princeton University (1934-1946) Professor Einstein was also at Princeton but at the Institute for Advanced Study.

An incident which occurred in 1943 may be of interest. During the war Professor Einstein was frequently consulted on technical matters, and on one occasion with Dr. Stephen Brunauer, who was in charge of research on high explosives for the navy, I spent some time discussing various technical questions with Professor Einstein in his office. At noon we walked out through what had been a lawn but in wartime was planted to soybeans. I guessed the nature of the crop, having been reared on a farm, but to confirm my opinion I plucked part of a vine and asked Professor Einstein what it was. He didn't know. As we passed by the gardener sitting on his wheelbarrow, he confirmed my judgment. Even Professor Einstein failed to solve those problems he chose not to think about. Although he had walked through this garden four times a day since the crop had been planted he had probably never consciously noticed it.

Five years after Planck's discovery that Newton's laws do not apply to very small particles, Albert Einstein in 1905 showed they also don't apply to bodies that are moving at speeds approaching the velocity of light. Experiments performed by the physicist, Michelson, and the chemist, Morley, at Case Institute of Technology in Cleveland, raised a dilemma which contradicts Newtonian mechanics and requires the special theory of relativity to explain it. They showed that light moves past an observer on the earth at the same speed no matter which way the earth is itself moving. This was as disconcerting as if a train passed a person riding in a car at the same speed no matter which way the car travelled. This could only be rationalized by assuming that speed by itself causes meter sticks to shorten and slows clocks in a special way that could be represented by a set of equations called the Lorentz transformation, after a famous Dutch physicist who devised the equations describing this behavior.

Einstein took all of these results and developed them into the special theory of relativity. There have been many confirmations of his theory but none is more spectacular than the confirmation provided by the exploding atomic bombs and the hydrogen bombs. Thus Einstein could say in 1905 that when matter disappears it must reappear again in the form of energy and that this energy is in a fixed proportion to the matter lost. This is expressed by an $E = mc^2$. This means that the energy produced in ergs is equal to the mass disappearing in grams multiplied by the velocity of light expressed in centimeters per second, squared. This is one of the great triumphs of human thought.

In this connection it is interesting to recall the statement in Doctrine and Covenants 137:7-8 that spirit is a more refined form of matter. This might well have troubled the materialists of an older generation, but now that we know of the interchangeability of energy and matter, such difficulties disappear. When one contemplates the wonders of the universe, it is natural to have faith in an omnipotent Creator. This seems also to have been Einstein's point of view.

The special theory of relativity developed the laws of mechanics for bodies passing each other at a fixed rate of speed. If, however, the speed changes, as when a body falls toward the earth, a more general set of laws is required. This more general set of physical laws, which among other things helps one understand the force of gravity, constitutes Einstein's general theory of relativity. The general theory is a powerful tool which astronomers use in discussing the history of the universe.

There is one riddle which has puzzled scientists for a generation. The whole universe seems to be expanding. The evidence for this is interesting. If light is emitted from a body moving toward you it is more violet than if the body stands still, while if the body is moving away the light emitted is redder. This is called the Doppler effect. This same effect exists for sound. Thus if a train whistles while it is coming toward you it is higher pitched than if it were stationary, while the pitch is lower if the train whistles while it is going away. Since the light from the stars is redder than it would be if they were stationary we must conclude they are moving away from us. The stars farther away show the greater red shift. From the rate at which the universe is expanding, George Gamow, among other scientists, calculates back to when all the stars were in a lump together and it comes out to be over a billion years ago. Fred Hoyle at Cambridge University, on the other hand, thinks that matter is being continuously created to compensate for the expansion and so the universe retains the same density. The correct conclusion to be drawn seems to be that the scientific theory of the origin of the universe is still unsettled but the question is nevertheless extremely interesting.

Curiously enough, Einstein received the Nobel Prize for explaining how light plucks electrons out of a metal and hurls them out into space. To do this, he used quantum theory rather than relativity. This is an indication of the universality of his genius.

On one occasion when I was with Professor Einstein, he expressed interest in the ethical teachings of Confucius, but was not particularly interested in the doctrinal teachings of the religions with which he was acquainted. Although he was very loyal to the Jewish people and was a Zionist, he had lost interest in their religious practices. In spite of this, he was religious.

On another occasion, Professor Hugh S. Taylor and I were taking Professor Einstein and an Israeli chemistry professor to Professor Einstein's home in a car. The subject turned to religion and I explained to Professor Einstein our LDS belief in a pre-existence. He immediately asked about the pre-existence of animals. I explained our belief that everything was created spiritually before its temporal existence. This interested him, but the conversation was terminated at the end of the journey.

In a paper "On Physical Reality" (1936) Einstein said: "The most incomprehensible thing about the world is that it is comprehensible." Addressing a Conference on Science, Philosophy and Religion (1940), Einstein says that belief in regularity in nature, to which he subscribes, belongs to religion. To quote:

> To this [sphere of religion] there also belongs the
> faith in the possibility that the regulations valid for the

world of existence are rational, that is, comprehensible to reason. I cannot conceive of a genuine scientist without that profound faith. The situation may be expressed by an image: science without religion is lame, religion without science is blind.

The book *Albert Einstein, Philosopher-Scientist* by Paul Arthur Schlipp (Tudor Publishing Company), provides a mine of information on this great scientist.

PART VIII

Truth in Brief

Truth in Brief

FOR ME THERE HAS BEEN NO SERIOUS DIFFICULTY IN reconciling the principles of true science with the principles of true religion, for both are concerned with the eternal verities of the universe.

Believe everything scholars can strictly prove and suit yourself about the rest.

Science has nothing to say one way or the other about whether there is a spirit. . . . The evidence lies outside of our present scientific knowledge.

Another avenue to religious faith lies in the examination of the evidence. "By their fruits ye shall know them" is a test to which the Restored Gospel is daily subjected.

This is a wonderful world indeed for those who can see clearly or, lacking this, are able to walk by faith.

All of us are tempted at times to give easy answers. We are asked for bread and we give our questioner a stone. This is usually because we just do not know the correct answers.

One of the many things the Restored Gospel has done is to emphasize, as the scriptures have always done, the deep personal concern of God for His children.

The fact that we are alive disposes of the many weighty arguments that might otherwise be adduced to prove that human life in all its complexity could not exist. Also, the wonder of being born into this world makes one discount arguments that rule out our rebirth into immortality on the ground that it would be too complex.

I believe that every brilliant conquest made by man is but a manifestation of the divine spark which sets him apart from the rest of creation. Man is in the image of God, destined to go on learning and perfecting himself throughout eternity.

God would be less compassionate than many good men if life ended at the grave. Broken, incomplete lives are the best possible reason for a hereafter in which the scales of justice are balanced by a just God. To believe otherwise is to attribute to God a lack of the sensitivity that we find regularly in good men. Such a supposition is incredible to me.

Since the need for prophetic guidance still persists, I find it natural to believe it is still present in the contemporary world and so I accept as modern scripture the prophetic writings of today.

Apparent contradictions between religion and science often have been the basis of bitter controversy. Such differences are to be expected. As long as human understanding approaches the Divine will all seeming contradictions disappear. Such complete understanding is to be approached as a part of the eternal progress we will continue in the life to come. In the meantime, we can only continue our quest for the balanced view that comes from weighing all evidence carefully in the search for enduring values. The road is a long one, but the outcome is assured if we are willing to travel it.

The purpose of living is to grow in wisdom and goodness, and this growth is possible because God gives man freedom to choose. This freedom necessarily gives man the opportunity to make wrong choices as well as right ones.

I have often met this question: "Dr. Eyring, as a scientist, how can you accept revealed religion?" The answer is simple. The Gospel commits us only to the truth. The same pragmatic tests that apply in science apply to religion. Try it. Does it work?

Henry Eyring receiving National Medal of Science from President Lyndon B. Johnson, February 6, 1967.

. . . Non-intervention in human affairs is not a sign of the absence of God or His disinterest. Rather, it exemplifies one of His greatest gifts, that of free agency which enables us to work out our individual salvation. If Lucifer were ruling the world, no one could doubt his presence.

Obedience to Gospel principles can make a man master of himself, and thus of his own destiny; There is no greater freedom than that. . . . Nothing of importance is ever accomplished by man except by obedience to correct principles. Obedience is . . . the price of freedom.

There is a deep meaning running through all that touches our lives. The Gospel is to be found not only in the scriptures, but in every detail of the world if we can but read it.

The Christian doctrine of the worth of the individual has largely made possible the freedom under which science has flourished.

It is the great mission and opportunity of religion to teach men "the way, the truth, the life," that they might utilize the discoveries of the laboratory to their blessing and not to their destruction. There is need for added spirituality of the kind that leads to brotherhood, to go hand in hand with the scientific progress of our time.

Some people have pointed to some member of the Church and said, "Now, Dr. Eyring, that's one of your brethren, and he's not what he ought to be." My answer is this, "Well, you ought to see what he would be like if it weren't for the Church." We have to keep firmly in mind at all times the two aspects of the Church, its divinely-inspired perfect side, and its human side.

The things we believe are only a part of the things that are yet to be revealed, and if we do our part our position is sure. We will indeed be exalted in the celestial kingdom and have the blessings which the Lord has promised for those who are faithful.

Index